Course 1 Student Edition

Second Edition

Math Innovations Course 1

MOVING MATH FORWARD THROUGH CRITICAL THINKING AND EXPLORATION

At This Rate

Focusing on Ratios, Proportions and Statistics

Linda Jensen Sheffield

Suzanne H. Chapin

M. Katherine Gavin

ACKNOWLEDGMENTS

Math Innovations Writing Team

Authors

Linda Jensen Sheffield
Suzanne H. Chapin
M. Katherine Gavin

Project Manager

Janice M. Vuolo

Teacher Edition Team

Alice J. Gabbard
Jacob J. Whitmore
Ann Marie Spinelli

Writing Assistants

Jane Paulin
Kathy Dorkin

Mathematics Editor

Kathleen G. Snook

Assessment Specialist

Nancy Anderson

Advisory Board

Jerry P. Becker
Janet Beissinger
Diane J. Briars
Ann Lawrence
Ira J. Papick

Cover photo of girl dancing by TSI Graphics.
Unless otherwise noted, all images on cover and interior used under license by ShutterStock, Inc.

www.kendallhunt.com
Send all inquiries to:
4050 Westmark Drive
Dubuque, IA 52004-1840
1-800-542-6657

ISBN 978-1-4652-1256-6

Production Date: 7/18/2014
Printed by: King Printing Co., Inc.
Lowell, Massachusetts
United States of America
Batch number: 431256

Printed in the United States of America
2 3 4 5 6 7 8 9 10 17 16 15 14

At This Rate:
Focusing on Ratios, Proportions and Statistics

Table of Contents

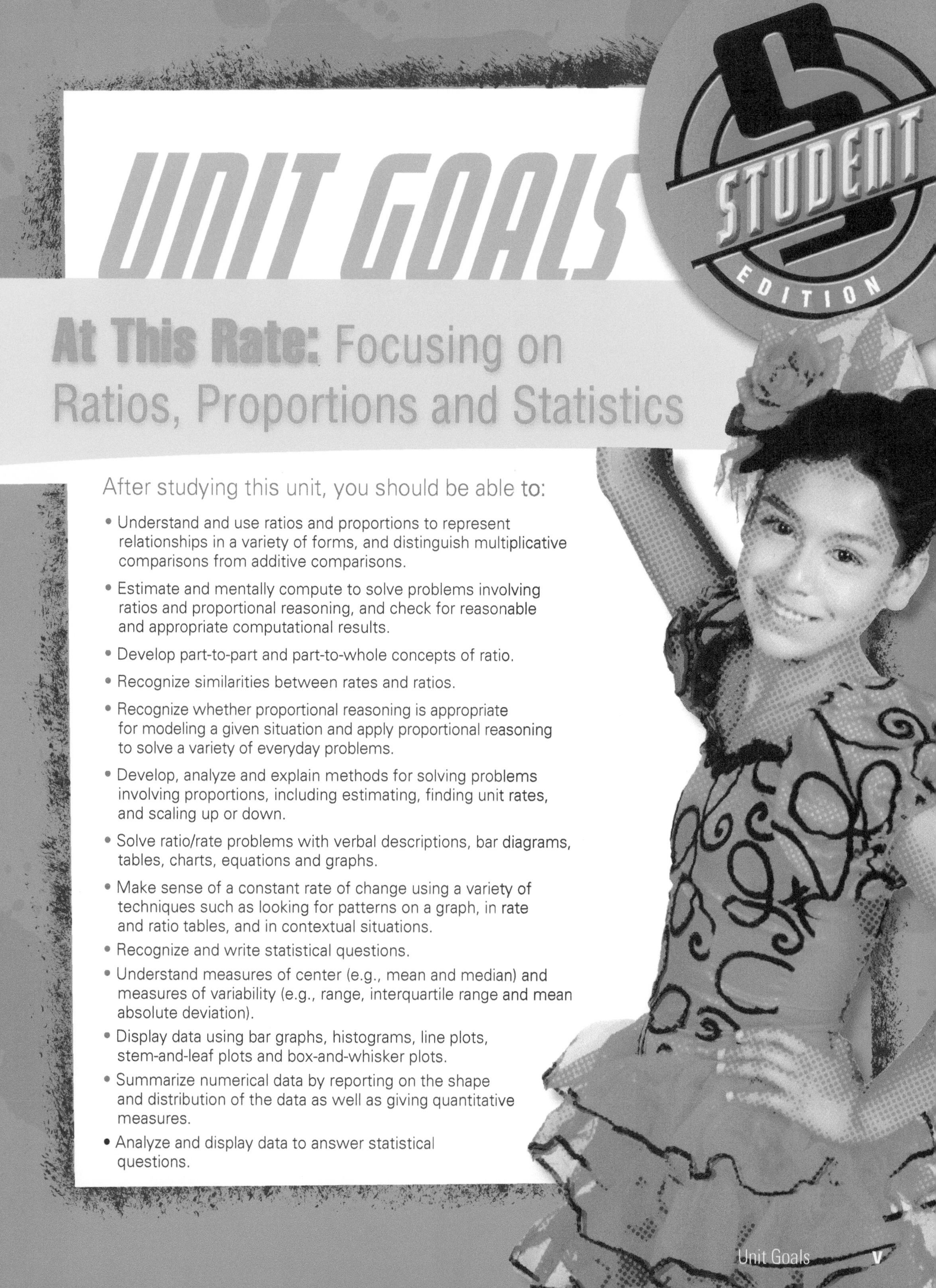

UNIT GOALS

At This Rate: Focusing on Ratios, Proportions and Statistics

After studying this unit, you should be able to:

- Understand and use ratios and proportions to represent relationships in a variety of forms, and distinguish multiplicative comparisons from additive comparisons.
- Estimate and mentally compute to solve problems involving ratios and proportional reasoning, and check for reasonable and appropriate computational results.
- Develop part-to-part and part-to-whole concepts of ratio.
- Recognize similarities between rates and ratios.
- Recognize whether proportional reasoning is appropriate for modeling a given situation and apply proportional reasoning to solve a variety of everyday problems.
- Develop, analyze and explain methods for solving problems involving proportions, including estimating, finding unit rates, and scaling up or down.
- Solve ratio/rate problems with verbal descriptions, bar diagrams, tables, charts, equations and graphs.
- Make sense of a constant rate of change using a variety of techniques such as looking for patterns on a graph, in rate and ratio tables, and in contextual situations.
- Recognize and write statistical questions.
- Understand measures of center (e.g., mean and median) and measures of variability (e.g., range, interquartile range and mean absolute deviation).
- Display data using bar graphs, histograms, line plots, stem-and-leaf plots and box-and-whisker plots.
- Summarize numerical data by reporting on the shape and distribution of the data as well as giving quantitative measures.
- Analyze and display data to answer statistical questions.

In *At This Rate: Focusing on Ratios, Proportions and Statistics*, you will follow a group of students as they solve problems involving ratios, proportions and data in preparation for a festival. These topics are often described as the gateway to higher mathematics including algebra, geometry, probability and statistics. They are also critical to becoming an intelligent consumer.

At the start of this unit, you will begin to explore proportional reasoning. You will make comparisons based on multiplication and division rather than on addition and subtraction. For example, let's say that you want to find the faster runner: Bailey or Roy. Bailey runs the 100-meter dash in 12 seconds and Roy runs the 200-meter dash in 25 seconds. You could subtract and say that Roy took 13 seconds longer than Bailey, but this does not tell you who is faster. With proportional reasoning, you could divide 200 meters by 25 seconds and say that Roy ran 8 meters each second. You could then use either multiplication or division to determine if Bailey ran more or fewer meters per second. This problem, as with many others in this unit, might be solved in a variety of ways. Can you think of another way? This is just one example of the type of reasoning that you will be doing throughout this unit.

Later in this unit, you will learn how to answer statistical questions. You will explore how to summarize the data in sets and more importantly, how to create and interpret a wide range of displays such as dot plots, stem-and-leaf plots, histograms and box-and-whisker plots.

As you solve the problems in this unit, think about applications to your own life. You should find that proportional reasoning and statistics are applicable to an amazing range of problems, and the study of both topics will prepare you for higher-level mathematics as you move into high school and beyond. We hope you enjoy the journey!

Mathematically yours,
The Authors

Linda Sheffield Suzanne H. Chapin M. Katherine Gavin

Using Proportional Reasoning

Reasoning about, comparing and making sense of quantities and their relationships are important to your future success in algebra. You also use comparisons to determine the best deal and if everyone gets a fair share or fair pay. In this section, you will explore how using multiplication and division to compare quantities builds on many of the ideas you have developed so far this year.

Comparing without Computing

Jason and Jill are running. They both start at the same place and end at the same place. Jill runs faster than Jason.

1. Who reached the end first?
2. What if Jason reached the finish line before Jill? How could this be? Write down as many reasons as you can think of.
3. Share your list with a partner. What assumptions did you make to answer Question 1?

Do you ever jump right into a problem without stopping to think about the question? In this lesson, you will use reasoning and estimation before you solve a problem. Take your time and think before using a pencil or calculator!

The International Festival

Eastside Middle School is having an International Festival. They plan to have food and refreshments from around the world. The students decided to make lemonade for their festival. Lemonade is considered an all-American drink, but did you know it was quite popular in Egypt at the turn of the first millennium (around the year 1000)?

The lemonade in the two pitchers below is from the same large batch. Jonah is worried that they are going to run out of lemonade. He wants to add two cups of water to each of these pitchers.

1. If Jonah adds the water and stirs, will the lemonade in each pitcher taste the same as before? Will the lemonade in the two pitchers taste the same as each other? Talk to a partner and decide if the two pitchers of lemonade will taste the same.
2. Sadie thinks that the lemonade is already too weak. Instead of adding water, she wants to add three scoops of lemonade mix to each pitcher and no more water. If she does this, will the lemonade in the two pitchers taste the same as before? Will they taste the same as each other? Discuss this with your partner.

You may have studied concentrations in your science class. Concentration is the amount of one substance in another substance. Notice that when you compared concentrations of lemonade, you had to think about two sets of two things—the amount of lemonade mix and the amount of water in the first pitcher and the amount of lemonade and the amount of water in the second pitcher.

You can use pennies and squares of paper to think about concentrations. First place six pennies on a 2" × 2" square of paper. Then place the same number of pennies on a 4" × 4" square of paper. Spread out the pennies evenly on both squares. In the small square, there are six pennies for 4 square inches of paper. In the large square, there are six pennies for 16 square inches of paper. There is a greater concentration of pennies on the small square.

3. How many pennies would you have to place on the larger square for the concentrations to be the same?

Now place the number of pennies you found in Question 3 on the large square.

4. If you add four pennies to each square, will they still have the same concentration of pennies? Discuss this with a partner.

5. Suppose the small square and larger square start with the same concentration of pennies, and then you attach another 2" × 2" paper square to each and spread out the pennies evenly. Will they still have the same concentration of pennies? Discuss this with a partner.

6. Make up questions comparing the concentration of the pennies. Then share your questions with a partner or group.

Population density is a measure of the concentration of people in a given region. In other words, population density tells you how crowded a region is. A population density is the number of people per fixed unit of area, like 1 square mile or 1 square kilometer. When you compare population densities, you again have to think about two sets of two things—the number of people in the first group and the area of the space they occupy and the number of people in the second group and the area of the space they occupy. Using population densities lets you compare how crowded two regions are even if the populations or areas of those regions are very different.

Comparing Populations

As part of the International Festival, several classes will represent countries from around the world. The students are arguing about which country is the largest. China has the greatest population in the world. Russia has the greatest area.

7. Which country, China or Russia, would you say is the largest? Explain your choice.

8. How could you determine which country on average is more crowded?

9. The total areas of China and the United States are almost the same. China has about four times as many people as the United States.

    a) Which country is more crowded? How can you show this with the pennies and squares?

    b) Do you need to know the area and population of each country to know this? Why or why not?

10. The population densities of Brazil and Chile are about the same. Brazil has more than ten times the area of Chile. Discuss each question with a partner.

    a) What do you know about the number of people in Brazil compared to the number of people in Chile? Explain.

    b) Imagine that 100,000 people move to each country. Will each country have the same population density as before? Will they have the same population density as each other?

    c) Now, imagine that 100,000 people leave each country. Will the population density remain the same as before? Will the two countries have the same population density as each other?

You did not have to know the areas or populations to answer Questions 7–10. However, you can also use these numbers to make comparisons. You could compare using addition/subtraction or you could compare using multiplication/division. For example, let's examine the populations of Cambodia and Russia.

Country (2008)	Population	Rounded Population
Russia	141,822,000	
Cambodia	14,071,000	

Example 1

How many more people live in Russia than in Cambodia?

You can solve this problem using subtraction ($141{,}822{,}000 - 14{,}071{,}000 = n$) to find that 127,751,000 more people live in Russia than Cambodia. You could also think of this as addition.

$14{,}071{,}000 + 127{,}751{,}000 = 141{,}822{,}000$.

Example 2

How many times as many people live in Russia compared to Cambodia?

You can use either multiplication or division to make comparison.

$14{,}071{,}000 \cdot n = 141{,}822{,}000$ or $141{,}822{,}000 \div 14{,}071{,}000 = n$

11. Round the population of Russia to the nearest ten million. Round the population of Cambodia to the nearest million. Use these numbers to estimate how many times as many people live in Russia as in Cambodia.

We can also compare the areas of Russia and Cambodia.

Country (2008)	Approximate Area in Square Miles	Approximate Area in Square Kilometers
Russia	6,500,000	17,000,000
Cambodia	69,600	181,040

12. How much larger is Russia than Cambodia in square miles? What operation should you use to answer this question? Explain. How much smaller is Cambodia than Russia in square kilometers? What operation did you use?

13. How many times as large is Russia compared to Cambodia? Talk to a partner about which operation you should use to answer this question. Estimate whether Russia is about 10, 100, 1,000 or 1,000,000 times as large. Is your estimate the same if you use square kilometers instead of square miles?

14. Which country is more crowded? Be prepared to defend your answer.

Comparing in the Mini-Olympics

Another event in the International Festival is a mini-Olympics. You can do one of the mini-Olympic events with your class. Choose five players for a class paper tossing contest. Players will compete to see who has the best record for throwing a wad of paper into a wastebasket from five feet away. The first player will get three attempts. The second player will get six attempts. The third player will get nine attempts. The fourth player will get 12 attempts. The fifth and final player will get 15 attempts. Record their scores in a chart like this one.

Player's Name	Number of Tosses Made	Number of Tosses Attempted
		3
		6
		9
		12
		15

15. Who has the best record in your class paper tossing contest? Talk to your partner about your choice. Order the players from the best to the worst in the contest. Be prepared to defend your order in a whole-class discussion.

Several girls are practicing for a basketball tournament. Zoey and Alana each made the same number of baskets.

16. Can we say that Zoey and Alana are equally skilled? What else would you need to know to decide who is better?

17. Zoey has taken twice as many shots as Alana. With this information, can you now decide who is better? Discuss your answer with a partner.

18. Jasmine has taken twice as many shots as Zoey. How many baskets would she have to make to have the same shooting average as Zoey?

19. Jaime has made 20 baskets and Delaney has made 15 baskets.

- **a)** How many more baskets has Jaime made than Delaney? What operation did you use?
- **b)** Can you tell who is better at making baskets? Explain.

Wrap It Up

MATHEMATICALLY SPEAKING

- concentration
- population density

Talk to a partner about how to make comparisons without using numbers. For example, Australia and Romania have about the same population. The area of Australia is much larger than that of Romania.

- **a)** Which country is more crowded? What two things for each country did you have to consider?
- **b)** The area of Australia is about 32 times as large as the area of Romania. How do the population densities of the two countries compare?

LESSON 1.1

SECTION 1

On Your Own

Write About It

1. The approximate 2008 populations and areas of Singapore and Luxemburg are shown in the table.

Country	Population	Area
Singapore	4,588,600	707.1 square kilometers
Luxemburg	464,900	2586.0 square kilometers

a) Round and estimate to find how many times as many people live in Singapore compared to Luxemburg. What two operations might you use? Show both equations.

b) How many more square kilometers are there in Luxemburg compared to Singapore? What two operations might you use? Show both equations.

c) Without doing any additional calculations, figure out which country has the greater population density. Explain your reasoning.

2. Use the table to answer the following questions.

Name of County	Area in Square Miles	Human Population (2000 census)	Deer Population (2008 estimation)
Gallatin	98.8	7,870	4,350
Knox	387.6	31,795	5,425

a) How many more deer were there in Knox County than in Gallatin County? Show your work.

b) Victor said he would really like to see a deer. He wants to go to Knox County since they have more deer than Gallatin County. Is his reasoning correct? Which county would you choose if you wanted to see a deer? Explain.

c) Is one county more crowded with people? Use rounding and estimation to explain your thinking. Did you compare using addition/subtraction or with multiplication/division?

On Your Own

3. Ty Cobb and Pete Rose were two of the best hitters in the history of baseball. Ty Cobb had 4,189 career hits and Pete Rose had 4,256 career hits.

   a) Compare the number of career hits of the two players.

   b) Talk to a partner about the operation you used in Part a. Did you find more than one way to do this?

   c) To find a player's batting average, divide the number of hits by the number of times at bat. What other information would you need to figure out which player had the better batting average?

   d) Ty Cobb's batting average was .366. Could someone with 10 hits have a better batting average than Ty Cobb?

4. At noon at Eastside Middle School, 24 students and 1 teacher were in the 1,500-square-foot science lab. Four teachers and 96 students were in the 6,000-square-foot cafeteria. Which room was more crowded? Explain.

5. To paint three walls of her room, Chloe mixed 1 gallon of white paint with 2 gallons of blue paint. For the fourth wall, she mixed 1 quart of the same white paint with 2 quarts of the same blue paint.

   a) Will the walls be the same or different shades of blue?

   b) Chloe decides to add 1 quart of white to each of her first two mixtures. Will they now be the same shade of blue? Explain.

6. Roberto and Harrison are on the swim team for the mini-Olympics. Roberto swam his event in 38 seconds. Harrison swam his event in 1 minute and 5 seconds.

   a) Can you determine who swam faster in these events? Explain.

   b) Roberto's event was half the distance of Harrison's event. Can you now determine who swam his event faster?

7. The number of times a piano string vibrates in a second increases as the length of the string decreases. Which piano string would vibrate more slowly—a 36-inch string or a 24-inch string?

8. In 2008, the world population density was about 33 people per square mile of Earth, including the oceans. How does this compare to the population density of the world, not including the oceans?

9. Calvin and Homer raced a 50-yard dash, and Calvin won by 5 yards. The next time, they each ran at the same speed as before, but Homer got a five-yard head start.

   a) Who won this time? Explain.

   b) For the third race, Calvin and Homer ran at the same speeds as before. However, this time Homer ran 50 yards and Calvin started back 5 yards and ran 55 yards. Who won this third race? Explain.

10. The Stewarts are on a 240-mile trip. Let m represent the number of miles they have already traveled. Which expression represents the number of miles they have left to travel?

    A. $240 - m$

    B. $240m$

    C. $m + 240$

    D. $240 \div m$

11. Last month, Culver City recycled 6.2 tons of newspapers. This month they recycled 5.72 tons of newspapers. How many more tons did they recycle last month than this month?

12. Which of the following is the greatest number?

    A. 32.4

    B. 30.405

    C. 32.39

    D. 32.04213

13. Write 84 as a product of prime numbers.

14. What is the distance between A and B on the number line below?

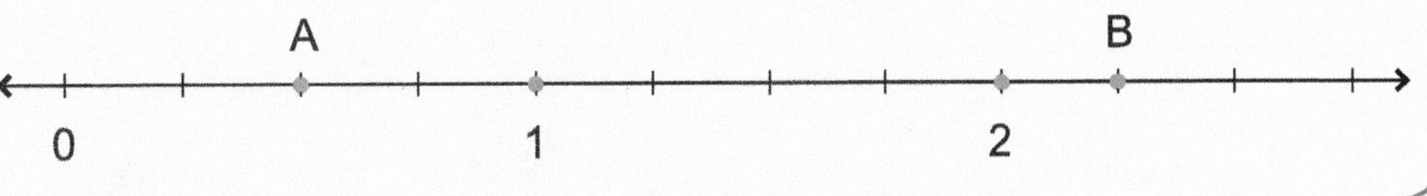

LESSON 1.2

Parts and Wholes

Start It Off

The decorating committee for the International Festival plans to put flowers in vases on each table in the cafeteria. They are putting 2 roses, 3 carnations and 4 tulips in each vase. They will need a total of 108 flowers. How many roses will they need?

Hint
See page 150

The Decorating Committee

In this lesson, you will use ratios to make comparisons.

MATHEMATICALLY SPEAKING

- ratio
- part-to-whole
- part-to-part

Let's Review

Ratios compare or relate two or more quantities. When you compare two quantities, ratios are written in one of three forms: as a fraction $\left(\frac{a}{b}\right)$, using a colon ($a:b$) or with words (a to b). The fraction notation usually means a part-to-whole comparison. The colon and word notations often indicate a part-to-part comparison. All three notations can be used for any type of ratio, so you should use the context of a problem to determine which type of comparison is being made.

There are 6 boys and 3 girls on the decorating committee for the festival. Each of the following represents the ratio of the number of boys to the number of girls.

6 to 3 $\qquad$ 6 : 3 $\qquad$ $\frac{6}{3}$

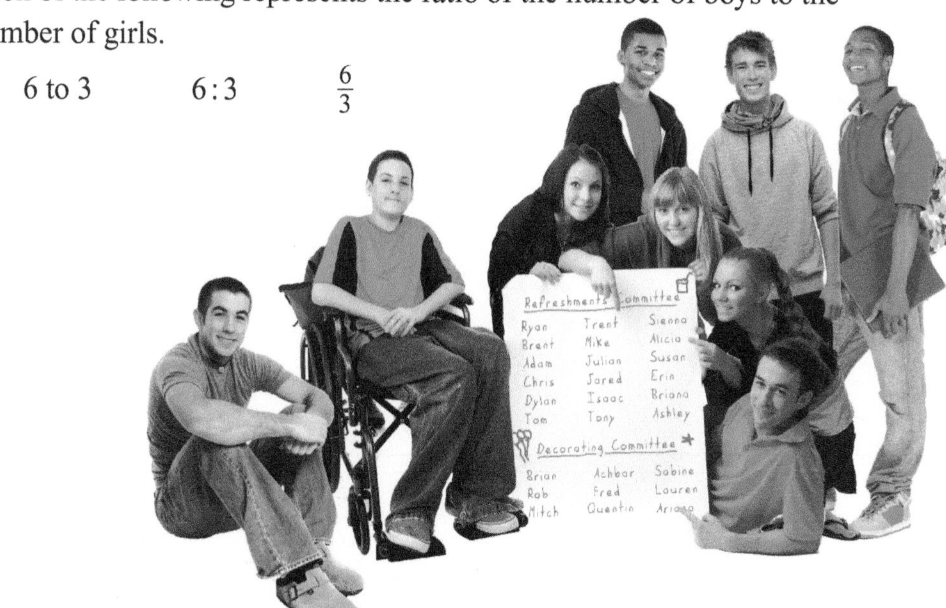

1. Write the ratio of girls to boys in three different ways. How do these ratios compare to the ratio of boys to girls? Did you use a part-to-part or part-to-whole ratio?

The ratio of boys to students on the committee is 6 boys to 9 students. You can write this as 6 to 9, 6:9 or $\frac{6}{9}$.

2. What is the ratio of girls to students on the committee? How does this compare to the other ratios? Is this part-to-part or part-to-whole ratio?

The students on the decorating committee might be shown like this. You might also show the students using a bar diagram.

6 boys	3 girls
Total = 9 students	

3. The refreshments committee for the International Festival has 12 boys and 6 girls.
   a) Compare the ratio of boys to girls on the decorating committee to the ratio of boys to girls on the refreshments committee. What do you notice?
   b) Write both ratios in fraction form. Simplify the fractions. What do you notice?
   c) There is another committee that has three times the number of boys and three times the number of girls as the decorating committee. What is the ratio of boys to girls on that committee? Write this as a fraction in simplest form. Compare this to your ratios for the other two committees. What do you notice?
   d) Another committee has n times the number of boys and n times the number of girls as the decorating committee. How does the ratio of boys to girls on the new committee compare to the ratio of boys to girls on the decorating committee? Explain. Give two examples using different values for n.

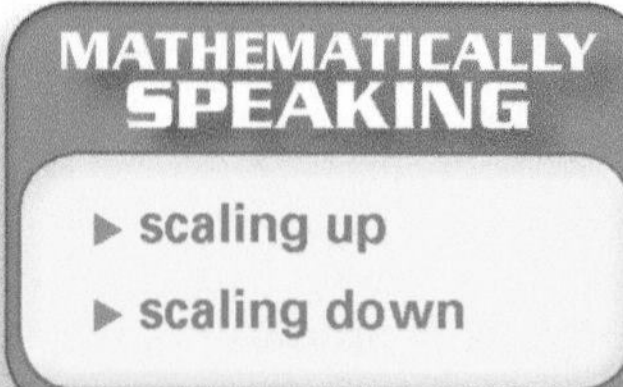

This ratio of boys to girls can be shown with a diagram. Notice how the following diagrams of each committee compare. Scaling up is when you multiply both numbers in a ratio by any number greater than 1 to get a new ratio. The refreshments committee has the same ratio of boys to girls as the decorating committee, but its membership is scaled up by a factor of 2.

Decorating Committee

Refreshment Committee

Scaling down is when you divide the numbers in a ratio by any number greater than 1 to get a new ratio. For example, a ratio of 4 girls to 6 boys could be scaled down by dividing both numbers by 2. This would give you an equivalent ratio or 2 girls to 3 boys.

4. A team of two boys and 1 girl represent the United States at the International Festival.

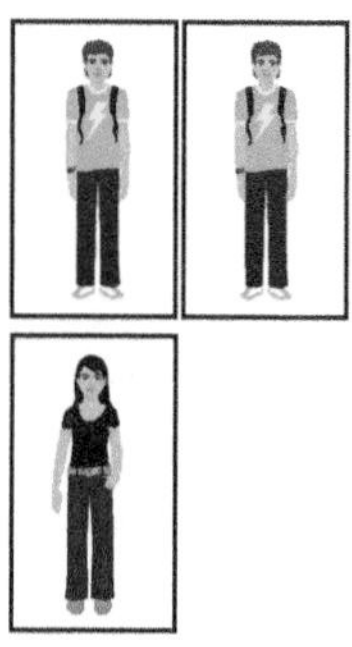

a) Start with the ratio of boys to girls in the decorating committee. What number should you divide both parts of this ratio by to get the ratio of boys to girls representing the United States?

b) What is the ratio of boys to girls representing the United States? How does this compare to the ratios of boys to girls on the decorating and refreshments committees?

c) Draw a bar diagram for the students representing the United States.

d) Write the ratios of girls to boys for each of the three groups as fractions. What do you notice?

e) Write the ratio of boys to the total number of students for each of the three groups. Discuss your observations with a partner.

MATHEMATICALLY SPEAKING

- equivalent ratios
- simplest form
- proportion

Equivalent ratios are ratios that show the same multiplicative comparison between two values. We can write ratios as fractions in simplest form to check whether they are equivalent. An equation that states that two ratios are equal is a proportion. Note that in a proportion, you are considering the relationship between two ratios, and each ratio is a comparison of two things.

5. The team representing Russia in the International Festival has 5 boys and 3 girls.

a) Is the ratio of boys to girls on the Russian team equivalent to the ratio of boys to girls on the U.S. team? Explain.

b) The team representing China has more students than the team representing Russia, but an equivalent ratio of boys to girls. One possibility for the number of boys and girls on the Chinese team is 10 boys and 6 girls. You could write this proportion as:
5 boys: 3 girls = 10 boys: 6 girls or $\frac{5 \text{ boys}}{3 \text{ girls}} = \frac{10 \text{ boys}}{6 \text{ girls}}$.
What's another possible number of boys and girls on the team representing China? Write a proportion to show that the ratio of boys to girls is the same as that for the Russian team. How might you use the following to find another equivalent ratio?

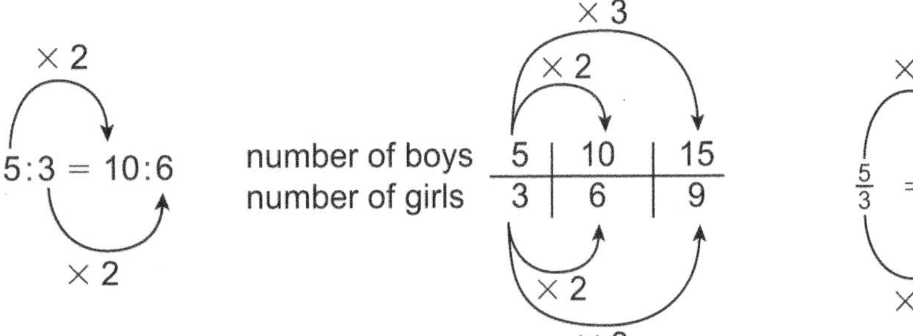

6. The team representing Brazil at the International Festival has a boy-to-girl ratio of 2 : 1. The Brazilian team has a total of 45 students.

2 parts boys	1 part girls
45 students	

a) How many are boys and how many are girls?

b) How many more boys than girls are there on the Brazilian team?

c) Write the ratio of girls on the Brazilian team to the total number of students on the team.

7. a) Copy and complete the table.

Committee	Boys	Girls	Total Number of Students	Ratio of Girls to Total Number of Students
Decorating	6	3		
Refreshments	12	6		
U.S. Team	2	1		
Brazilian Team			45	

b) Write the ratio of girls to the total number of students for each group as a fraction. Are these part-to-whole or part-to-part ratios? What do you notice about them? Are these ratios equivalent? That is, do they form a proportion?

c) Another team has the same ratio of boys to girls as the Brazilian team. This new team has a total of 60 students. How many more boys than girls are on the new team? Explain your thinking.

The Refreshments Committee

The refreshments committee is making colcannon, a popular dish in Ireland. The ingredients for the recipe are shown here.

Colcannon

3 cups finely shredded green cabbage
4 cups mashed potatoes
$\frac{1}{4}$ cup water
$\frac{1}{4}$ cup milk
$\frac{1}{4}$ cup butter
Salt and pepper to taste

8. The students have decided to scale up this recipe to make more servings. They will use the same ratios of ingredients as the original recipe. They plan to use 1 cup each of water, milk and butter.

a) In this recipe, what is the ratio of cups of water to cups of milk?

b) What will the students have to multiply the amount of each ingredient by if they use 1 cup each of water, milk and butter?

c) How many cups of shredded cabbage and mashed potatoes will they need in the scaled up recipe?

d) What is the ratio of cups of shredded cabbage to cups of mashed potatoes in the original recipe? What is this ratio in the scaled-up recipe? Are these ratios equivalent?

9. Copy and complete the chart below.

Colcannon

Number of Recipes	Cups of Cabbage	Cups of Mashed Potatoes	Cups (each) of Water, Butter and Milk
1	3	4	$\frac{1}{4}$
2			
3			
4			
5			

a) What patterns do you notice?

b) What is the ratio of cups of shredded cabbage to cups of mashed potatoes for each recipe?

c) The number of cups of cabbage in a scaled-up recipe is 8 fewer than the number of cups of mashed potatoes. How many cups of cabbage and mashed potatoes were used in this scaled-up recipe?

10. It takes 6 large potatoes to make 4 cups of mashed potatoes.

a) Add a column for (unmashed) potatoes to your chart from Question 9.

b) How many potatoes will be needed if 10 cups of shredded cabbage are used? Be prepared to explain your thinking.

More Lemonade

Some students are making lemonade using the same powdered lemonade mix. Some of them like a stronger lemonade taste than others.

11. Copy and complete the chart below. Write each ratio in simplest form.

Person	Scoops of Lemonade Mix	Amount of Water	Ratio of Scoops of Lemonade Mix to Cups of Water
Noah	1	1 quart = ______ cups	
Victoria	2	______ pints = 8 cups	$\frac{2 \text{ scoops}}{8 \text{ cups}}$, 2:8 or 1 to 4
Hailey	3	$\frac{1}{2}$ gallon = ______ cups	
Caleb	5	______ gallons = ______ cups	$\frac{5 \text{ scoops}}{24 \text{ cups}}$, 5 to 24
Jayden	4	______ quarts = ______ cups	$\frac{1 \text{ scoop}}{3 \text{ cups}}$, 1 to 3

12. Work with a partner to decide which lemonade will taste the strongest. Will any of the lemonades taste the same? Order the lemonades from the weakest to the strongest.

13. Everyone now makes a new batch of lemonade using one gallon of water. They use the same ratio of lemonade mix to water as each used before. How much lemonade mix would each person use? Now compare the strengths of the lemonade in each gallon of lemonade.

14. Everyone makes a third batch, using 12 scoops of lemonade mix. They use the same ratio of lemonade mix to water as each used before. How much water would each person use? Again, compare the strength of the lemonade in each gallon of lemonade.

A lemonade recipe uses 5 scoops of lemonade mix for every 8 cups of water.

a) Talk to a partner about how much water should be added to 10 scoops of mix.

b) How much mix would you add to 20 cups of water?

c) How much mix would you add to 2 cups of water?

MATHEMATICALLY SPEAKING

- equivalent ratios
- part-to-part
- part-to-whole
- proportion
- ratio
- scaling down
- scaling up
- simplest form

LESSON 1.2 SECTION 1

On Your Own

1. Ariana used 5 scoops of lemonade mix to make 6 quarts of lemonade. Wyatt used 4 scoops to make a gallon of lemonade. Using two different methods, explain which lemonade had the stronger flavor.

2. The ratio of girls to boys on the entertainment committee is 8 to 5.

   a) Draw a bar diagram and a diagram with stick figures to show this relationship.

   b) What does the ratio 5 : 13 describe about this committee?

   c) Is the ratio 8 : 5 the same as the ratio 5 : 8? Label each part of the ratio to describe what the numbers represent on this committee.

   d) If there are 52 students on the entertainment committee, how many are girls?

   e) If there are 15 more girls than boys on the committee, how many students are on the committee?

See page 150

3. The ratio of Steven's height to Addison's height is 5 : 4. Express Addison's height as a fraction of Steven's height.

4. At the International Festival, bratwurst, a German sausage, will be served. The ratio of the number of boys to girls who named bratwurst their favorite food was 5 : 3.

   a) Write this ratio two different ways, using the word *to* or as a fraction.

   b) What is the ratio of the number of girls to students who named bratwurst as their favorite?

   c) If 15 boys named bratwurst their favorite, how many students named bratwurst their favorite?

   d) If you know there are 12 fewer girls than boys that named bratwurst, how many boys named bratwurst?

See page 150

On Your Own

5. Write each ratio as a fraction in simplest form.

   a) 24:36

   b) 14 to 35

   c) $\frac{4}{22}$

Questions 6–8 refer to the chart below.

Favorite International Foods			
Type of Food	Number of Students Naming It as Their Favorite	Type of Food	Number of Students Naming It as Their Favorite
Pad Thai from Thailand	40	Fish and Chips from England	80
Pizza from Italy	230	Tacos from Mexico	200
Greek Salad	150	Paella from Spain	100

6. Jasmine wrote one ratio from the table as 2:1. What might Jasmine be comparing? Find more than one possibility and label each part of your ratio. Explain how the order of the numbers in the ratio makes a difference.

7. One hundred parents are also coming to the festival. The parents chose favorite foods in the same ratio as that of the students. How many parents chose pad thai as their favorite?

8. José wrote one ratio from the table as $\frac{1}{4}$. What was he comparing?

9. Alejandro drew the following diagrams to show $\frac{2}{3}$:

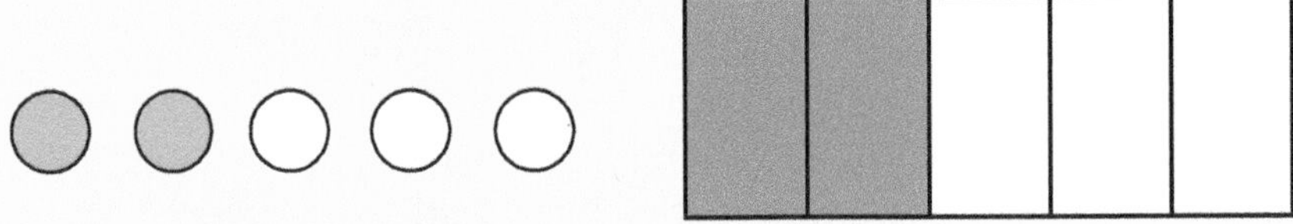

   a) Explain how Alejandro's diagrams show $\frac{2}{3}$.

   b) Matilda said she thought the diagrams were a good way to show $\frac{2}{5}$. Explain.

   c) List two other ratios that might be used to describe these diagrams. Label the parts in each ratio.

   d) Why is it important to label the parts of a ratio written as a fraction?

10. Decide whether each of the following compares one part to another, one part to the whole or the whole to one part. Write a ratio for each. Be sure to include the labels for your ratio. The first one is done for you.

   a) Of the 230 sixth-grade students at Eastside, 47 ride their bikes to school.

      This compares the number of students in the whole sixth grade to the number in the part of sixth graders who ride bikes. One way to write this whole-to-part ratio is 230 sixth-graders : 47 bike riders.

   b) For every 5 students who walk to school, 18 ride the bus.

   c) The length of a giraffe's neck is half its total height.

   d) The width of a red deer's antlers is $\frac{3}{5}$ the length of its body.

   e) Write your own examples of a part-to-part and a part-to-whole ratio.

11. Pedro is making a rhubarb and strawberry cobbler. The recipe says to use 6 cups of fresh rhubarb and 4 cups of fresh strawberries. Pedro has only 4 cups of rhubarb. Sierra says he should use 2 cups of strawberries. Do you agree? Explain.

12. Chloe planted 8 pepper plants in a 12-foot row and 6 tomato plants in a 10-foot row. Which row had plants closer together? Explain.

13. Micah has 35 goldfish in a 15-gallon fish tank. Ruby has 20 goldfish in a 12-gallon fish tank. Whose fish tank is more crowded? Explain.

14. The ratio of goldfish to koi in a pond is 18 to 12. If there are a total of 45 goldfish and koi in the pond, how many more goldfish than koi are there? Show your work.

15. The ratio of peanuts to cashews in a trail mix is 2 : 1. The ratio of peanuts to raisins is 3 : 2. What is the ratio of cashews to raisins?

See page 150

16. Carson's money jar has only dimes and quarters. For every 4 dimes, there are 6 quarters. There is a total of $4.75 in the bank. How many dimes does he have?

17. In 2009, the ratio of Grandpa Jensen's age to his son's age was 2 : 1. Twenty-five years ago, the ratio was 3 : 1. In what year was Grandpa Jensen born? Explain your reasoning.

On Your Own

18. Milk is on sale for \$1.58 for 2 quarts or \$3.32 for a gallon. Which is the better buy?

19. Aiden used the following spices in his apple pie recipe:
    - $1\frac{1}{3}$ teaspoons cinnamon
    - $\frac{1}{4}$ teaspoon nutmeg
    - $\frac{1}{8}$ teaspoon salt

    a) How many teaspoons of spices did he use altogether?

    b) Complete Aiden's chart showing the amount of spice he would need for several apple pies. Include an explicit rule for *n* pies.

Number of Pies	Tsp. of Cinnamon	Tsp. of Nutmeg	Tsp. of Salt
1	$1\frac{1}{3}$	$\frac{1}{4}$	$\frac{1}{8}$
2			
3			
4			
n			

20. Gabriella, Kylie and Lily each had the same number of beads. Gabriella put 7 beads onto each necklace she made and had 1 left over. Kylie put 10 beads onto each necklace she made and had none left over. Lily put 8 beads onto each necklace and had two left over. What number of beads might they have started with?

    A. 64 **C.** 60

    B. 74 **D.** 50

21. Show your steps to complete the following divisions.

    a) $0.7254 \div 0.03$

    b) $0.00525 \div 21$

22. Find n:

    a) $\frac{n}{8} = 30$ **d)** $4 \cdot (n + 3) = 40$

    b) $46 = n - 38$ **e)** $\frac{n + 4}{2} = 15$

    c) $\frac{15}{n} = 3$

LESSON 1.3

Comparing and Computing

Start It Off

Ratios can be used to represent the relationship between measures. Use the table below that compares number of centimeters to number of inches to answer the following questions.

Centimeters	2.54	5.08	7.62	10.16	12.7
Inches	1	2	3	4	5

Copy and fill in the blanks.

1. **a)** The ratio of centimeters to inches is ____________________.

   b) For every inch, there are ____________________ centimeters.

2. Is the ratio of centimeters to inches a part-to-whole or a part-to-part ratio? ____________________

3. 7.62 : 3 compares ____________________ to ____________________ and is equivalent to the ratio ____________________.

4. If you have 6 inches, the equivalent number of centimeters is ____________________.

5. True or false?

   a) $c = 2.54i$, where c represents the number of centimeters and i represents the number of inches.

   b) $i = 2.54c$, where c represents the number of centimeters and i represents the number of inches.

6. How is the relationship between centimeters and inches shown on a ruler?

In this lesson, you will continue to make comparisons using ratios and proportions. You will compare ratios by writing them as fractions and decimals. In all problems, estimate first when making numerical comparisons. After computing, compare your answers to your estimates to see if your answers make sense.

Human Proportions

The sixth grade class is investigating art around the world for the International Festival. They found that around 1487, Leonardo da Vinci drew the famous Vitruvian Man. He used mathematics to draw what was thought to be the ideal man. He found ratios between different body parts that were fairly consistent on men of varying heights. A few of the ratios da Vinci used in his drawing were:

- 1:16 The ratio of the width of a man's fingers to the length of his foot
- 1:1 The ratio of the length of a man's outspread arms to his height
- 1:10 The ratio of the length of a man's face to his height
- 1:3 The ratio of the length of a man's ear to the length of his face
- 1:4 The ratio of the width of a man's shoulders to his height

Meredith wanted to know if the ratio between any of her measurements would match these. She measured the length of her ear to be $2\frac{1}{2}$ inches. Her face is 7 inches long. Meredith said that the ratio was $2\frac{1}{2}$ to 7. She did not know how to compare this to the ratio found by da Vinci.

1. Isabella said that she could compare Meredith's ratio of length of ear to length of face to da Vinci's ratio by multiplying. She said that since da Vinci's ratio of ear length to face length is 1:3, she could multiply the length of Meredith's ear by 3. If the result is the length of her face, then Meredith's ratio is the same as da Vinci's. Try Isabella's method. Is Meredith's ratio of ear length to face length 1:3? Explain.

2. Jacob said he could compare the ratios by scaling up. He says you can double the measurements of Meredith's ear and face and compare that ratio to da Vinci's. Will the ratio you get by scaling up the ratio $2\frac{1}{2}$ to 7 be equivalent to da Vinci's ratio of 1:3? Explain.

3. Simon wrote the ratio of the length of Meredith's ear to her face as $\frac{2.5''}{7''}$. He then used division to change the fraction to a decimal. What decimal did he get? Is this equivalent to the ratio da Vinci used? Explain.

4. With a partner, choose one of the ratios that da Vinci used in his drawing. Measure the two body parts named in the ratio on one person.

   a) Record your measurements and find the ratio. Compare the ratio you found to the one used by da Vinci. Are they equivalent?

   b) Talk about different methods you could use to compare the ratios. Do you prefer drawing pictures, multiplying, comparing fractions, scaling up or down, comparing decimals or another method? Does it depend on the ratio?

   c) Repeat the measurements on the other partner. Is the ratio of these measurements the same as daVinci's ratio? Did you use the same method to compare the ratios this time as you did in Part a?

Da Vinci found that many ratios were the same when measuring adult men. This is not the case when comparing humans to other animals. For example, the length of an African elephant's ears is about $\frac{1}{2}$ of its height.

5. Compare the ear length to height ratio of the African elephant to the same ratio for da Vinci's Vitruvian Man.

Wrap It Up

Mr. Sheffield's shoulders are 20 inches wide, and he is 6 feet tall. Talk to a partner about how to compare the ratio of his shoulder width to his height to the ratio used by da Vinci for the Vitruvian Man. Think about multiplying, comparing ratios written as fractions or decimals, scaling up or down, or another method. Do all methods give the same comparison? Explain.

Hint
See page 150

LESSON 1.3 SECTION 1

On Your Own

1. A three-inch frog can hop 60 inches.

   a) What is the ratio of the length of the frog to the length it can hop? If you could hop like a frog, with the same ratio of your height to the length you can hop, how far could you hop? Show your work using at least two different methods. Compare your methods. Did you get the same answer? Did you prefer one method over another? Explain.

   b) The frog is $\frac{1}{4}$ foot long and can hop 5 feet. Does the ratio between the length of the frog and the length of its hop change when the units change? Show this using scaling up and/or scaling down and another method.

2. A female house spider can travel 33 times its body length in one second. If the ratio of the distance you could travel in one second to your height were the same as the spider's, how far would you travel in one second? Show your work.

3. A shrew weighs about $\frac{1}{5}$ ounce and eats about $\frac{3}{5}$ ounce each day. Andres weighs about 52 kg. If the ratio between his body weight and the amount he eats each day were the same as the shrew's, how much would he eat (in kg)?

4. In 2005, Josh was 5 and his father was 7 times as old as he was.

   a) How old will Josh and his father be in 2015?

   b) When do you use addition or subtraction in this problem and when do you use multiplication or division?

On Your Own

5. Several Eastside Middle School students are practicing for the mini-Olympics.

   a) Grant and Omar are running at the same speed around a track. Grant started first. When Grant had run 8 laps, Omar had run 6 laps. If they continue at the same speed, how many laps will Omar have run when Grant runs 12 laps?

   b) Ashlyn and Alondra are also running around the track. They are long-distance runners and never change their pace once they start. Both girls start at the same time. When Alondra completes 8 laps, Ashlyn completes 6 laps. How many laps will Ashlyn have run when Alondra has run 12 laps?

   c) Compare and contrast the two situations. What operation did you use to answer each question?

6. The arm length of the Statue of Liberty from her shoulder to her wrist is 42 feet. If the ratio of the length of the Statue of Liberty's arm to the length of her thumb is the same as yours, how long is her thumb? Show your work.

7. The Hercules beetle is sometimes considered the strongest creature on earth. An average Hercules beetle weighs 25 grams. Some people claim that the ratio of the beetle's weight to the amount it can lift is 1:850.

   a) If this is true, how much can a Hercules beetle lift?

   b) Find something that is about 850 times the weight of the average Hercules beetle. Do you believe the beetle can lift this much? Do further research to confirm or deny this claim.
   Note: 1 kg = 2.2 pounds.

8. The golden rectangle is often seen in art and architecture. It has a very special relationship between the length and width. Write a report on its construction and applications.

9. During the basketball game, Sacra made 7 free throws out of the 10 she attempted. What percent of the free throws did she miss?

   A. 10%

   B. 30%

   C. 50%

   D. 70%

10. In the Foreign Language Club, each person speaks one language in addition to English. 15% speak French, $\frac{2}{5}$ speak Spanish, 0.2 speak German and the rest speak Chinese. Which language is spoken by the most students?

11. What is the area and the perimeter of the following figure?

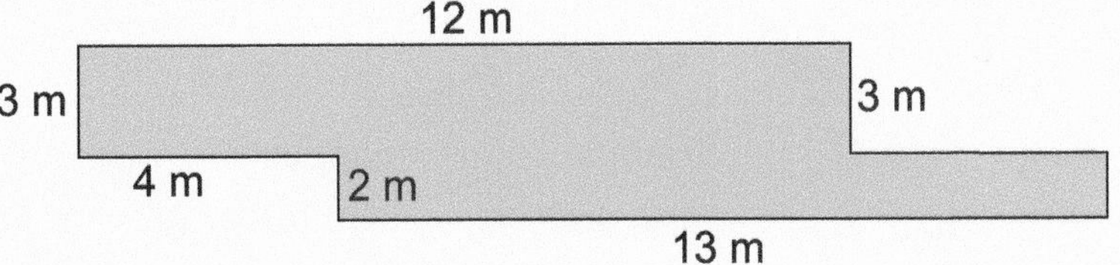

12. Marianne has 3 red chips, 5 blue chips, 1 green chip and 6 yellow chips in her pocket. What is the ratio of blue chips to all the chips in her pocket?

   A. $\frac{1}{5}$

   B. $\frac{1}{3}$

   C. $\frac{5}{10}$

   D. $\frac{10}{15}$

13. Solve for n.
   $n = 5^2 + 4(8 - 2 \div 3) + 2$

LESSON 1.4 Fair Shares

Start It Off

Jeremiah made 67 of the 82 baskets he attempted during his team's basketball games. His teammate Cole made 23 of the 25 baskets he attempted. Is it fair to say that Jeremiah is a better shooter? Explain.

Sharing Prizes

For the International Festival, several students made their favorite trail mix to use as prizes for the games.

Winning teams at the festival won trail mix and shared it equally among the team members. The number of team members and the pounds of trail mix won for each competition are shown in the chart.

Competition	Number of Team Members	Pounds of Trail Mix to Share
Swimming relay team	4	5
Chess team	6	9
Academic team	8	10
Volleyball team	5	9
Table tennis team	2	3
Robotics team	6	10
Basketball team	10	12

1. Did all winners receive the same amount of trail mix? Talk to a partner about how you might determine this.

a) Lily said that if 4 members of the swim team got 5 pounds, then 2 members got 5 pounds ÷ 2, or 2.5 pounds. She wrote the proportion $\frac{5 \text{ pounds}}{4 \text{ people}} = \frac{2.5 \text{ pounds}}{2 \text{ people}}$. She said that the members of the table tennis team each got more trail mix because their 2 members get 3 pounds $\left(\frac{3 \text{ pounds}}{2 \text{ people}}\right)$. Use Lily's method to figure out how much trail mix 2 people on the chess team got. Compare this amount to the amount of trail mix that 2 members of the swim team got and to the amount that 2 members of the table tennis team got.

b) Max said it is easy to compare the amount of trail mix that each member of the volleyball team got to the amount of trail mix that each member of the chess team got because each team got the same total amount of trail mix. Who got more trail mix, each member of the volleyball team or each member of the chess team? How might you use Max's method to compare the amount of trail mix each member of the table tennis team got to the amount received by each member of the volleyball team or by each member of the chess team?

c) Julio used benchmarks, like $\frac{1}{2}$ or 1. For example, he said that if the winning swim team got 5 pounds for 4 people, then each member got more than 1 pound. He then used division to figure the exact amount one person got. He found $5 \div 4$ to find that each person got $1\frac{1}{4}$ pounds of trail mix. He wrote the proportion $\frac{5 \text{ pounds}}{4 \text{ people}} = \frac{1\frac{1}{4} \text{ pounds}}{1 \text{ person}}$. Work with a partner to determine the amount of trail mix received by each winning team member. Complete the chart.

Competition	Number of Team Members	Total Pounds of Trail Mix to Share	Pounds of Trail Mix for Each Team Member $\left(\frac{\text{pounds}}{1 \text{ person}}\right)$
Swimming relay team	4	5	$\frac{5 \text{ pounds}}{4 \text{ people}} = \frac{1\frac{1}{4} \text{ pounds}}{1 \text{ person}}$
Chess team	6	9	
Academic team	8	10	
Volleyball team	5	9	
Table tennis team	2	3	
Robotics team	6	10	
Basketball team	10	12	

d) Order the winning teams from those whose members each received the least amount of trail mix to those whose members each received the greatest amount. Be prepared to share your thinking with the class.

2. How many pounds of trail mix would the chess team have to win in total so that each player would get the same amount of trail mix as each player on the swimming relay team? Explain.

3. The basketball team has 10 players and the soccer team has 15 players. They have 20 pounds of trail mix to split between both teams so each player gets the same amount.

20 pounds of trail mix	
basketball team = 10 players	soccer team = 15 players

a) Is there enough trail mix for each player to get a pound? Will each player get at least a half-pound of trail mix? Explain.

b) How many pounds of trail mix will each team get?

c) How many pounds of trail mix will each player get?

d) Compare your solution and your method to those of your partner. Were your answers and methods the same?

Wrap It Up

Describe some of the methods you used for comparing ratios to see how much trail mix an individual team member received. Don't forget to explain how you used division and scaling ratios up and down to form equivalent ratios.

LESSON 1.4 SECTION 1

On Your Own

Write About It

1. Mitchell had the following math quiz scores.

   Quiz 1: 15 points received out of 20 points total

   Quiz 2: 18 points received out of 25 points total

   Quiz 3: 8 points received out of 10 points total

   Quiz 4: 45 points received out of 50 points total

   a) Compare Quiz 1 and Quiz 3 by scaling up so each quiz has the same total number of points. On which quiz was his grade better? Explain.

   b) Compare Quiz 1 and Quiz 4 by scaling up to an equal number of points received. On which quiz was his grade better? Explain.

   c) Find each quiz grade as a decimal rounded to the nearest hundredth and as a percent using a ratio of $\frac{\text{points received}}{\text{points total}}$. On which quiz was his grade the best? Explain.

2. The refreshments committee is serving pizza. A table of 10 people is served 4 medium pizzas and a table of 6 people is served 2 medium pizzas. If everyone at each table shares equally with the others at their table, will each of the 16 people get the same amount of pizza? Explain with words, diagrams and ratios.

3. Jake and his two brothers have 2 pounds of peanuts to share equally. Hannah and her three sisters have 3 pounds of peanuts to share equally.

   a) Will each girl or each boy receive more peanuts?

   b) What is the difference between the weights of the peanuts each boy gets and the peanuts each girl gets? Show your work.

4. Each sixth-grade homeroom elects one representative for the Student Council. In Mr. Jacob's homeroom, Gert got 18 votes from a class of 30. In Ms. Zimmer's homeroom, Patrick got 15 votes from a class of 24. Gert said she did better than Patrick because she got 3 more votes. Support Patrick's claim that he did better.

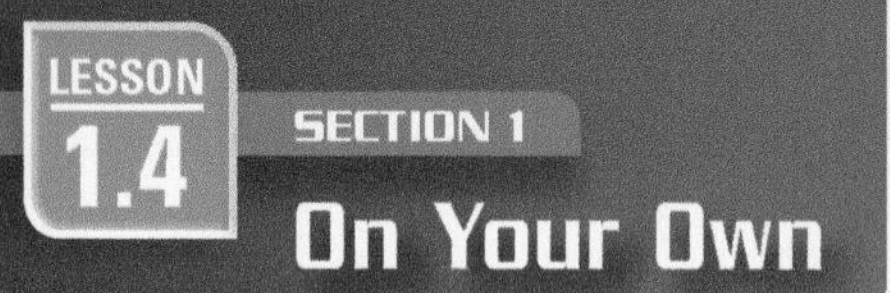

On Your Own

5. Jade has been practicing free throws. So far this week, she has made 40 out of 120 shots. She plans to attempt 80 more shots today. How many of her 80 shots will she have to make in order to make 50% of her shots this week?

6. Aaliyah and Makayla also practiced free throws. Aaliyah made 8 of 11 shots, and Makayla made 35 of 50 shots. Each girl said she did better than the other. Give a reason that supports each girl's claim.

7. The ratio of inches to centimeters is $\frac{1 \text{ inch}}{2.54 \text{ centimeters}}$. Use proportions to complete the chart with equivalent measures.

Inches	Centimeters
5.2	
	5.08
$2\frac{1}{2}$	

8. Jayla and Krista made lemonade from a powder mixed with water. Then, they poured it into two pitchers. The smaller pitcher has 2 quarts of lemonade in it and the larger pitcher has 5 quarts of lemonade in it.

   a) Jayla adds 2 cups of water to the lemonade in the smaller pitcher without adding more powder. How much water would she have to add to the lemonade in the larger pitcher so its ratio of powder to water is the same as the ratio in the smaller pitcher?

   b) Next, Krista adds 3 scoops of lemonade mix to the lemonade in the smaller pitcher without adding water. How much mix would she have to add to the lemonade in the larger pitcher so its ratio of powder to water is the same as the ratio in the smaller pitcher?

   c) If you know that the original lemonade was made using 1 scoop of lemonade mix for every 4 cups of water, how much lemonade mix would Jayla have to add to the smaller pitcher along with her 2 cups of water from Part a so her lemonade would have the same ratio as before? How much water would Krista have to add to the smaller pitcher along with her 3 scoops of mix from Part b so the lemonade would have the same ratio as before?

9. Mr. Garcia's class makes a \$5 profit on each T-shirt, and Ms. Evans's class makes a \$3 profit on each T-shirt. Copy and complete the table to show the profits made for their T-shirt sales.

Number Sold by Each Class	Profit for Ms. Evans's Class	Profit for Mr. Garcia's Class	Total Profit
1	\$3	\$5	\$8
2	\$6	\$10	\$16
3			
4			
5			
6			
7			
8			
n			

10. **a)** Using the table in Question 9, what is the ratio of the profit made by Ms. Evans's class to the profit made by Mr. Garcia's class when each class sells 1 T-shirt?

    b) What is this ratio when each class sells 5, 8 or 10 T-shirts?

    c) What is the ratio if each class sells n T-shirts?

    d) Does this ratio change as the number of T-shirts sold increases?

11. If both Mr. Garcia's and Ms. Evan's classes sell the same number of T-shirts, how many T-shirts has each class sold when the total profit for the two classes is \$120?

On Your Own

12. On November 17, 2012, the world population was 7,052,713,968. It was predicted that the world population would be about 113 million people more than this by January 1, 2015. What total population was predicted for January 1, 2015?

13. How many vertices, edges and faces does this pentagonal pyramid have?

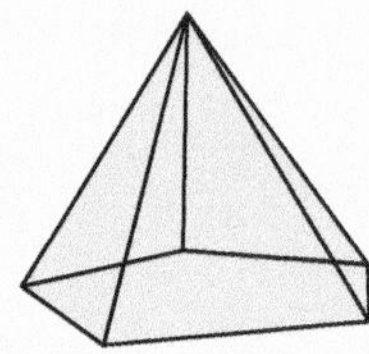

14. Which of the following recursive rules could be used to create this number pattern?

    16, 36, 46, 51 . . .

    A. Multiply by 2, and then add 4.
    B. Add 20.
    C. Divide by 2, then add 28.
    D. Add 2, then multiply by 2.

15. Which equation is true if $n = 4$?

    A. $5n - 12 = 8$
    B. $14 = n - 10$
    C. $5 = n - 9$
    D. $20n = 5$

16. Six out of the 25 students in Bob's class are in the Spanish club. What percent of the students in Bob's class are in the Spanish club?

Comparing Using Diagrams

MATHEMATICALLY SPEAKING
▶ profit

It is important for people to make sure that they are paid a fair wage for the work they do or that they make a fair profit on the items or services they sell. In this lesson, you will explore how ratios and proportions can help people make decisions about pay and profit.

Start It Off

In 1876, when *The Adventures of Tom Sawyer* was published, Aunt Polly might have paid a total of $1.25 to have her fence painted. Tom and Huck painted the fence. While Huck painted steadily for 4 hours, Tom only painted for a total of 1 hour.

- How much should Tom have been paid if the money was split fairly?
- Compare your answer to a partner's. Did you get the same answer? Did you use the same method?

Fair Shares for a Fundraiser

After the International Festival, students decided to donate money to UNICEF, the United Nations Children's Fund. Ms. Nguyen's class and Mr. Williams's class are competing to see who can raise the most money.

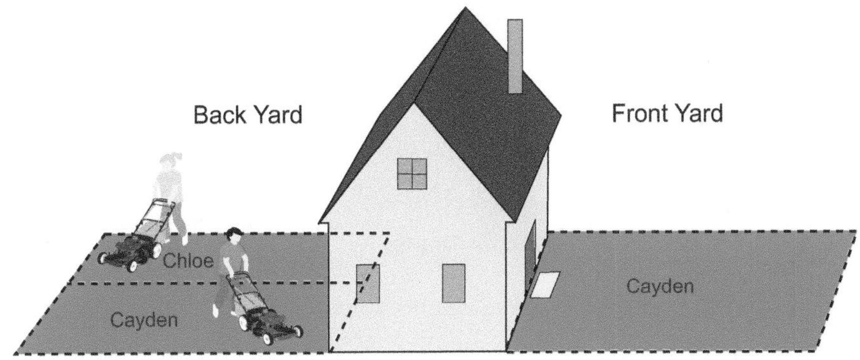

1. Cayden is in Ms. Nguyen's class and Chloe is in Mr. Williams's class. Mr. Taylor paid them $16 to mow his lawn. Cayden mowed the front lawn by himself, and he and Chloe each mowed half of the back lawn. The front and back lawns are the same size. How should Cayden and Chloe split the money? Use this diagram in your solution.

Hint
See page 150

Total amount mowed = 1 lawn	
____ mowed by Cayden	____ mowed by Chloe
$ ____ earned by Cayden	$ ____ earned by Chloe
Total amount paid = $16	

NOTE Note that you can form proportions from the diagram to help you find a solution. For example, $\frac{\text{fraction mowed by Cayden}}{\text{1 whole lawn}} = \frac{\text{money earned by Cayden}}{\$16}$.

---

2. The Dippy Ice Cream Shop paid the students $250 to design the store's webpage. The ratio of the work done by Mr. Williams's class to the work done by Ms. Nguyen's class was 3 : 2. Talk to a partner about a fair way for the classes to split the money. Be prepared to share your reasoning using a bar diagram.

Total work done = 1 website	
Work done by Mr. Williams's class = ________ parts	Work done by Ms. Nguyen's class = ________ parts
$ _____ earned by Mr. Williams's class	$ _____ earned by Ms. Nguyen's class
Total amount paid = $250	

3. On Saturday, the two classes had a car wash. Six students from Ms. Nguyen's class each worked 5 hours, and 9 students from Mr. Williams's class each worked 4 hours. They earned a total of $132.

a) What is a fair way to split the money between the two classes?

Hint
See page 150

b) Discuss your reasoning with a partner. Did you both get the same answer? Did you use a bar diagram or another method?

4. Lillian, Bailey and Chase collected cans to recycle. For every 5 cans Lillian collected, Bailey collected 3 cans and Chase collected 2 cans. This can be written as 5 : 3 : 2. If the recycling center paid $29.80 for their cans, how should the students divide the money? Discuss with a partner how you can use a ratio and a bar diagram to solve this.

<table>
<tr><td colspan="3">Total Cans = 10 parts</td></tr>
<tr><td>Lillian = 5 parts</td><td>Bailey = 3 parts</td><td>Chase = 2 parts</td></tr>
<tr><td>$____ earned by Lillian</td><td>$_____ earned by Bailey</td><td>$_____ earned by Chase</td></tr>
<tr><td colspan="3">Total Received = $29.80</td></tr>
</table>

Oobleck Ratios

Kaden remembered the Dr. Seuss book, *Bartholomew and the Oobleck*, and then did some research. He learned to make oobleck—a substance that can act like a liquid or a solid—using a simple recipe. He decided to make and sell oobleck to raise money for UNICEF. One recipe called for 3 parts cornstarch to 2 parts water.

5. **a)** Write the ratio of cornstarch to water in two different forms.

   b) Complete the table so the ratio of cornstarch to water stays the same.

Cups of Cornstarch	3	6	9	12	15	18	
Cups of Water	2						n

   c) If Kaden has $1\frac{1}{2}$ cups of cornstarch, how much water should he use? What if he has 2 cups of cornstarch?

   d) Three cups of cornstarch weigh 1 pound. If Kaden uses 10 pounds of cornstarch to make oobleck, how much water should he use?

Hint

See page 150

   e) Kaden found these other recipes for making oobleck:

   - 2 pints of cornstarch for every $1\frac{3}{4}$ pints of water
   - $1\frac{1}{2}$ liters of cornstarch for every 1 liter of water
   - 10 cups of cornstarch for every 6 cups of water
   - 21 quarts of cornstarch for every 11 quarts of water

Do any of these recipes have the same ratio of cornstarch to water as the original recipe? Find their ratios of cornstarch to water and order them from largest to smallest. Compare your results to those of a partner.

See page 150

Warning: If you make oobleck, do NOT pour it down the drain! It will clog!

MATHEMATICALLY SPEAKING

- profit

Carly and Sergio baby-sat for the Lopez twins. Carly baby-sat for 6 hours. Sergio baby-sat for 3 hours more than Carly. Together they were paid $60. Talk to a partner about how you might use ratios and a bar diagram to determine a fair way for them to split the money.

LESSON 1.5 SECTION 1

On Your Own

Write About It

1. Gianna and Abigail make and sell bracelets to raise money. Gianna sells hers for $6 apiece and Abigail sells hers for $8 apiece.

   a) Copy and complete the chart to show the amount of money that each girl receives for selling her bracelets.

Number Sold by Each Girl	Amount Gianna Received	Amount Abigail Received	Total Received
1	$6	$8	$14
2			
3			
4			
5			

   b) List three different ratios in simplest form that describe this situation. Be sure to label each ratio.

   c) Describe a proportion you can use to find the missing values in the chart.

   d) Explain how to find the number of bracelets sold when both girls have sold the same number of bracelets and the total amount received is $126.

   e) If the girls have sold the same number of bracelets and Abigail has received $38 more than Gianna, how many bracelets has each sold? Show your work.

   f) What is the ratio of the amount Gianna receives for one bracelet to the amount that Abigail receives for one bracelet? What is this ratio if they each sell 10 bracelets? Does the ratio change when the number of bracelets changes? Explain.

2. The ratio of the number of hours that Cameron worked picking apples for a neighbor to the number of hours that Shelby worked was 6:4. Shelby's little sister, Natalie, also helped. Natalie only worked half as many hours as Shelby. All together, the three worked for 36 hours.

   a) Find the number of hours each girl worked using this bar diagram.

Cameron = 6 parts	Shelby = 4 parts	Natalie = ______ parts
Total hours worked = ______		

   b) If they made a total of $48, how should they split the money?

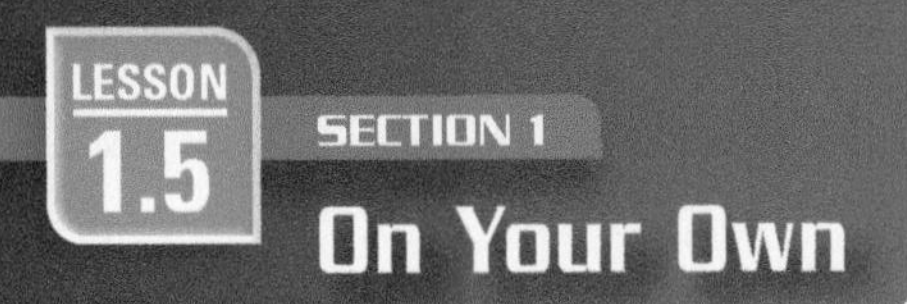

3. Dalton plans to make and sell "slime." His recipe uses 3 cups of water, 2 cups of glue and 1.5 teaspoons of borax.

   a) What is the ratio of water to glue?

   b) If Dalton has 1 cup of glue, how much water and how much borax should he use?

   c) 4 ounces of glue is $\frac{1}{2}$ cup. If Dalton has only 4 ounces of glue, how much water and how much borax should he use? Show your work.

4. The recipe for biodegradable plastic is $1\frac{1}{2}$ parts water to 1 part cornstarch and 5 drops of corn oil for every 2 tablespoons of water. When making this plastic, how much water and how much corn oil should you add to each of the following:

   a) 1 cup of cornstarch

   b) 2 tablespoons of cornstarch

   c) $\frac{1}{2}$ cup of cornstarch

See page 150

Warning: The plastic and the slime require cooking, which requires adult supervision. You can research the complete recipes on your own. If you make either of these, do NOT put it down the drain! It will clog!

5. A stack of 100 pennies is about 6 inches tall.

   a) Copy and complete the following ratio chart.

Number of Pennies	100	50	25	5	1	1,000		
Height of Pennies	6"						5 feet	1 mile

   b) If you had a million dollars in pennies in a single stack, would your stack be taller than the Empire State Building? Explain.

See page 150

6. For every \$3 Dalton saves, his father adds \$2 to his bank account.

   a) Make a part : part : whole ratio table that shows Dalton's total savings when Dalton has saved \$3, \$6, \$9, \$12, \$15 and *n* dollars.

   b) How much must Dalton save to have \$135 total in his account?

7. Ann adds 1 cup of rice to every 2 cups of water. If she uses 3 cups of water, how much rice should she add? Show the proportion you use.

8. Three brands of popcorn will make the following amounts.

Brand	Unpopped	Popped
Always Pops	2 cups	9 cups
Pop-Pop Popcorn	3 cups	13 cups
Crunchy Popcorn	4 cups	17 cups

Order the popcorn from the brand with the largest popped-to-unpopped ratio to the brand with the smallest ratio. Show your work.

9. To make biscuits, Tony uses 2 cups of flour for each $\frac{3}{4}$ cup of milk.

a) How much flour should Tony use with 3 cups of milk?

b) Write the ratio of flour to milk using whole numbers.

10. Nadia is mixing paint. She mixes 2 parts blue paint for every 1 part white paint. Complete the chart to show how much paint of each color she should use to make sure that all the paint has the same ratio of blue to white.

Blue Paint	1 quart	2 cups	3 gallons	_____ quarts
White Paint	_____ cups	_____ pints	_____ quarts	4 gallons

See page 150

11. It takes 5 leaves to feed two caterpillars each day. How many leaves will it take to feed 12 caterpillars for one day? Show the proportion you used.

12. Brenda, Elena and Miles have collected \$143 for UNICEF. The ratio of the amount of money Brenda collected to the amount Elena collected is 4 : 3. The ratio of Elena's amount to Miles's amount is 1 : 2. How much has each student collected? Show your work.

13. The ratio of the money that Roza, Mark and Viktor have is 4 : 2 : 5. Roza has \$15 more than Mark. How much money does Viktor have? Show your work.

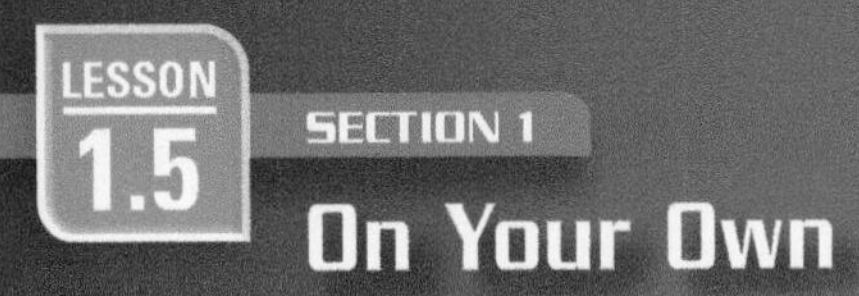

14. A pizza has a diameter of 18 inches. What is its radius?

    A. 9 inches
    B. 24 inches
    C. 36 inches
    D. 48 inches

15. Evaluate the expression $3^3 - 4^2$.

16. Carry's bedroom is 12 feet by 10 feet. Each wall is 8 feet high. She wants to paint all 4 walls. What is the total area that she has to paint?

17. Samuel read *s* books. Jacob read 3 more books than Samuel. Write an expression that shows the number of books that Jacob read.

18. Sketch and label a rectangular solid that measures 5 inches by 3 inches by 4 inches. What is the volume of this figure?

LESSON 1.6

Unit Price

As you've learned, ratios and proportions are useful when sharing money. They are also important when spending money. In order to be a smart consumer, you should know how to find a unit price and how to determine which choice is the best buy. If you want to pay a fair price, you probably want to find the best buy.

Which store has the best buy for grapes? Compare your answer to a partner's. Did you get the same answer? Did you use the same method?

Best Buy

The refreshments committee for the International Festival is planning to make fruit salad. Since they have a small budget and are planning to make a large fruit salad, they want to make sure they find the best prices.

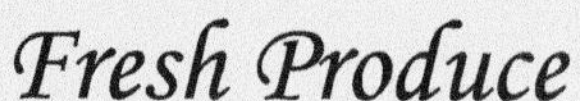

Fresh Produce

Bananas
3 pounds for $2.00

Peaches
3 pounds for $5.00

Apples
75¢ a piece

Strawberries
2 pints for $5

Green Grocers

Bananas
4 pounds for $3.00

Peaches
5 pounds for $10.00

Apples
3 for $2.00

Strawberries
1 quart for $6

FARMERS MARKET

Bananas
2 pounds for $1.50

Peaches
2 pounds for $3.00

Apples
5 pounds for $6.00

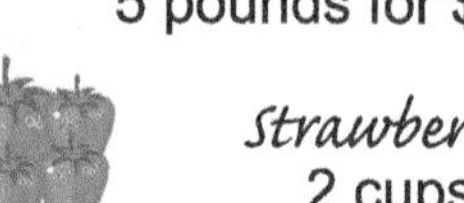

Strawberries
2 cups for $3

1. The fruit salad will be made from grapes, apples, strawberries, peaches and bananas. Work with a partner to determine which store has the best prices for these items. (The prices for grapes are in the Start It Off.) Be prepared to justify your choice.

One way to find the best price is to find a unit price. A unit price is the cost for one item or one unit, such as a pound.

Example

At Fresh Produce, since bananas are $2 for 3 pounds, I can divide $2 by 3 to find the cost for one pound. Since $\$2 \div 3 = \$0.67$, the unit price for a pound of bananas is $0.67 per pound (which can be written as $0.67 : 1 pound or $\frac{\$0.67}{1 \text{ pound}}$). This can also be written as 1 pound : $0.67 or $\frac{1 \text{ pound}}{\$0.67}$.

You can write the proportion $\frac{\$2}{3 \text{ pounds}} = \frac{\$0.67}{1 \text{ pound}}$. As always, the labels in the ratio are critical.

2. What is the price for 1 pound of bananas at Green Grocers and at Farmers Market? Write the unit price as a ratio in two different forms. Be sure to include the labels. Which of the three stores has the best price?

3. How many pounds of bananas can you get for $1.00 at each of the stores? How can you use your answer to determine which store offers the best price for bananas? Compare this to your answer to the previous question.

4. Malachi found the ratios $\frac{3}{5}$, $\frac{1}{2}$ and $\frac{2}{3}$ for the peaches at the three stores.

   a) What is the meaning of these ratios? Use these ratios to find the store with the best price for peaches. Show your work.

   b) Liliana found the ratios $\frac{5}{3}$, $\frac{2}{1}$ and $\frac{3}{2}$ for the peaches at the three stores. What do these mean? Use these ratios to find the store with the best price for peaches. Show your work.

   c) Why is it important to include the labels in ratios?

   d) Did either Liliana or Malachi find ratios that gave unit prices?

   e) How do you find the best buy when you know the price per pound? How is this different from finding the best buy when you know the number of pounds per dollar?

Pricing Supplies

The other committees for the International Festival also need to find the best price for their supplies. One committee plans to hand out pens and notebooks.

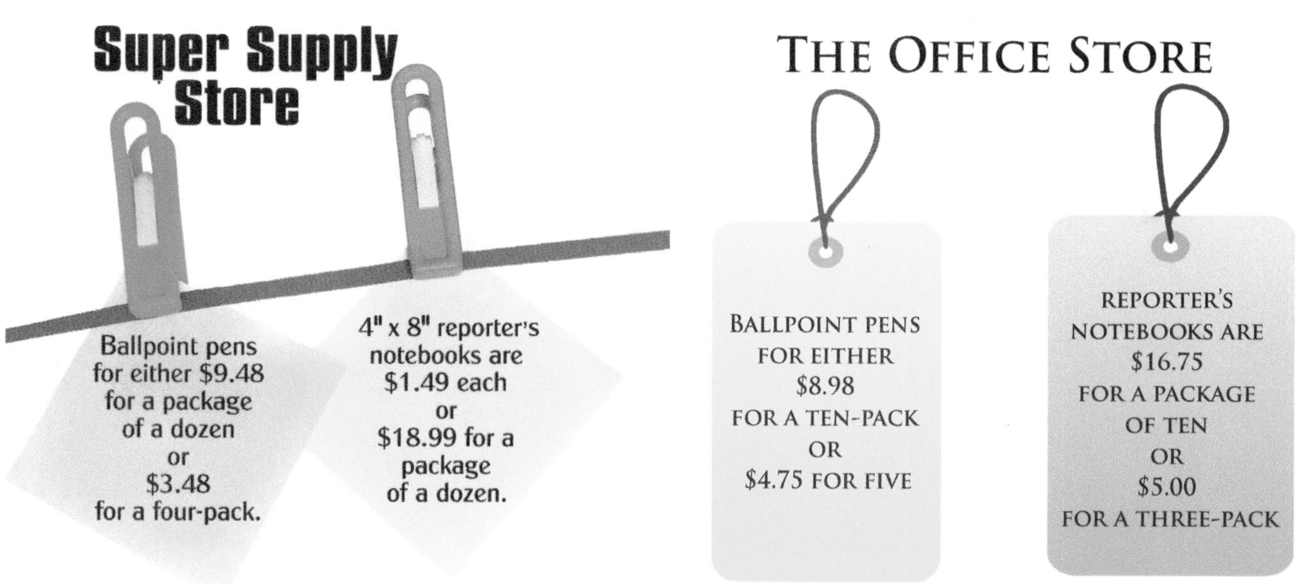

Use the ads above to answer Questions 5, 6 and 7.

5. Use estimation and mental computation to determine which is the best price. Be prepared to share your reasoning.

   a) \$9.48 for a dozen pens or \$3.48 for a four-pack

   b) \$8.98 for ten pens or \$4.75 for five

   c) \$1.49 for one notebook or \$5.00 for three

6. Find the unit price for 1 pen for each of the four packages. Find the unit price for 1 notebook for each of the four packages. Show your work, including any proportions.

7. The committee wants to buy 50 pens and 50 notebooks. Write a recommendation for the purchase. Give the total price and your reasons for your selection.

Wrap It Up

MATHEMATICALLY SPEAKING

- unit price

a) How can you figure out if a larger package has a better unit price than a smaller package?

b) When might it be better to buy a smaller package of something even if the larger package has a better unit price?

LESSON 1.6 SECTION 1

On Your Own

Write About It

1. At Super Saver, 6 ounces of red raspberries cost $2.50. At Mega Market, 1 pound of red raspberries costs $6.00.

   a) What is the unit price for 1 ounce of raspberries at each store?

   b) Explain how you would use the unit price to find the better buy.

   c) How many ounces of raspberries can you buy for $1.00 at each store?

   d) How could you use the ratio of ounces of raspberries to $1.00 to find the better buy?

   e) Compare your answers to Parts b and d. Which method do you prefer for finding the best price? Why?

2. A 12-ounce box of Corny Corn Flakes costs $3.14. A 20-ounce box costs $5.98. Which box is the better buy? Use proportions and unit prices to explain.

3. A quart of peach ice cream costs $2.49. A gallon of the same ice cream costs $10.56. Use rounding and estimation to find the better price. Explain.

4. Find the unit price for each of the following:

Item	Size	Price
a) Crackers	12 ounces	$3.29
b) Cookies	2 pounds	$5.80
c) Baked Beans	28 ounces	$1.80
d) Cheddar Cheese	8 ounces	$2.80

5. Bags of potatoes are on sale for the following prices.

Weight	2 pounds	5 pounds	10 pounds	20 pounds
Price	$1.00	$2.40	$4.85	$7.75

   a) Use rounding, estimation and mental calculation to list the bags in order from the least expensive per pound to the most expensive per pound.

   b) Find the unit price for 1 pound of potatoes for each bag.

On Your Own

c) Find the number of pounds of potatoes for $1.00 for each bag.

d) For each size bag, tell how much 20 pounds of potatoes would cost.

e) Compare these four methods for finding the best price. Would you get the same order from best to worst price with each method?

6. The mini-Olympics committee can buy a dozen baseballs for $29.95, a bucket of 30 for $79.85 or 4 for $10.75. Order these options from the least expensive to the most expensive using unit prices. Show your work.

7. Vincent worked 25 hours one week in July and earned $150. Gail worked 10 hours and earned $100. Whose rate of pay was better? Use the following methods.

   a) Estimate using a benchmark. Did each make at least $5 per hour? Did each make at least $10 per hour?

   b) Compare by using proportions. Scale up to determine how much each person would earn in 50 hours or 100 hours.

   c) Scale up to see how long it would take each person to earn the same amount of money. How long would Vincent and Gail each have to work to earn $300?

   d) Compare using a unit rate. How much did Vincent and Gail each earn in one hour?

   e) Did you get the same answer each time? Which method do you prefer? Why?

8. Ms. Brown paid $46.09 for 11 gallons of gas. How much did it cost per gallon?

9. Four 12-ounce boxes of cereal cost $10.00. Two 1-pound boxes cost $6.00. Which is the better buy? Explain.

10. Choose a fruit that is sold by the pound. Look at several grocery store advertisements to find which store has the best price. Write a paragraph about your findings.

Think Beyond

11. The ratio of the price of strawberries to the price of grapes is 5 to 3. Bill bought 4 pounds of grapes and 2 pounds of strawberries for $11. What was the unit price for a pound of grapes? Show your work.

Think Back

12. In a class of 12 boys and 14 girls, 15 students play basketball. How many boys might play basketball? Give a range from the least to the greatest possible number.

13. Compare the following using <, > or =.

a) −64 ______ −65

b) $\frac{3}{2}$ ________ $\frac{8}{7}$

c) −2 _______ absolute value of −2

d) opposite of −14 ________ −(−14)

14. Is it possible for two rectangles to have the same perimeter but different areas? Explain, and include an example.

15. If you add 7 to a number and then double your sum, you get 68. What was your original number?

16. Sandra is a birdwatcher. On Saturday, she saw 6 fewer than twice the number of birds she saw on Sunday. If she saw 8 birds on Sunday, how many did she see on Saturday?

A. 4 **C.** 20

B. 10 **D.** 2

Optional Technology Lesson for this section available in your eBook

SECTION 1

Sum It Up

In this section, you made comparisons by reasoning without using computation. You also made comparisons by using diagrams and by using multiplication and division. You learned different uses of ratios and proportions and learned to write ratios in a variety of forms. Finally, you explored a number of different strategies for comparing ratios including finding a unit price.

Thinking Proportionally without Computation

- You can use proportional reasoning to make a variety of comparisons. These comparisons involve a multiplicative rather than an additive comparison.
- You can use proportional reasoning to compare concentrations, population densities and sports statistics.

Concepts of Ratios and Proportions

- A ratio is a multiplicative comparison of two numbers. A ratio can show the relationship of one part to another part or of one part to a whole.
- Ratios can be written in three different ways: using a colon, using the word *to* or as a fraction. For example, a ratio comparing the number of boys in a class to the number of girls in the class when there are 15 boys and 12 girls might be written as 15:12, 15 to 12 or $\frac{15}{12}$.
- The order of the numbers in a ratio is important. The ratio of girls to boys in this same class is 12:15, 12 to 15 or $\frac{12}{15}$. The ratio of girls to the total number of students in the class is 12:27, 12 to 27 or $\frac{12}{27}$.
- Labels are often needed to clarify a ratio. For example, $\frac{12 \text{ boys}}{15 \text{ girls}}$ is different than $\frac{12 \text{ girls}}{15 \text{ boys}}$.
- Ratios may be written as equivalent fractions to find equivalent ratios. Equivalent ratios are ratios that show the same multiplicative relationship between two numerical values. For example, in this class the ratio of 12 girls to 15 boys may be written as an equivalent ratio of 4 girls for every 5 boys. This can be written as $\frac{12 \text{ girls}}{15 \text{ boys}} = \frac{4 \text{ girls}}{5 \text{ boys}}$. An equation that states that one ratio is equal to another is a proportion.

- Bar diagrams may be used to illustrate the part-to-part and part-to-whole relationships of ratios. For example, if there are 4 girls for every 5 boys and a total of 27 students, this may be shown as:

4 parts girls = 12 girls	5 parts boys = 15 boys
27 students total	

- Information about boys and girls in two classes of students may be shown using a table.

Class	Boys	Girls	Total Number of Students	Ratio of Girls to Total Number of Students
A	15	12	27	12:27, $\frac{\text{12 girls}}{\text{27 total students}}$
B	10	8	18	8:18, $\frac{\text{8 girls}}{\text{18 total students}}$

Note that the ratios of girls to the total number of students are the same in the two classes. These equivalent ratios form a proportion. $\frac{12}{27} = \frac{8}{18} = \frac{4}{9}$

- Ratios can be scaled up or scaled down to form equivalent ratios. Increasing and decreasing recipes is one example of this. For example, if a recipe calls for 2 scoops of lemonade mix for every quart of water, the recipe could be scaled up to 8 scoops of lemonade mix for 4 quarts of water.

Ratios and Proportions in Measurement

- Leonardo da Vinci used common ratios of body lengths to draw his Vitruvian Man. To determine if a 6' man with shoulders that are 18" wide has the same ratio of shoulder width to height as the Vitruvian Man with a 1:4 ratio, multiplication or division might be used. 18" • 4 = 72". Since 72" = 6', the ratio of shoulder width to height is 18:72, which is the same as a 1:4 ratio.
- Ratios and proportions can be used to compare measurements from different creatures. For example, if the ratio of the length of a frog's body to the length it can hop is 1:20, for a 6-foot man to have this same ratio of height to hop length, the man would have to be able to hop 120' for a 6:120 ratio.
- Ratios and proportions can also be used to convert from one measurement system to another. There are 2.54 centimeters for every 1 inch. This ratio can be scaled up to form equivalent ratios such as 5.08 to 2 and 10.16 to 4.

Comparing Ratios

Ratios can be compared using techniques similar to those used when comparing fractions. These techniques include using common numerators, using common denominators, comparing to benchmarks and converting to decimals.

- Part-to-part ratios can be compared by scaling up or down to match one of the parts. For example, you might compare Punch A, made with 3 cups of orange juice and 5 cups of pineapple juice, to Punch B, made with 6 cups of orange juice and 9 cups of pineapple juice. If you doubled the ingredients in Punch A, you would get 6 cups of orange juice and 10 cups of pineapple juice. So Punch A has a greater ratio of pineapple juice to orange juice than Punch B.
- Part-to-whole ratios can be compared by scaling up or down to match the total amount. For example, you might compare 5 cups of Punch C, made with 3 cups of orange juice, to 12 cups of Punch D, made with 9 cups of orange juice. You could triple the ingredients of Punch C to get 15 cups of punch made with 9 cups of orange juice. So Punch C has a lower ratio of orange juice to total punch than Punch D.
- Ratios can be compared by looking at benchmarks such as $\frac{1}{2}$ or 1. For example, you might compare 8 cups of Punch E, made with 3 cups of orange juice, to 9 cups of Punch F, made with 5 cups of orange juice. Punch F would have a greater ratio of orange juice to total punch than Punch E, because Punch F is more than half orange juice while Punch E is less than half orange juice.

Representing Ratio and Proportion Applications

- Bar diagrams can represent proportions and help determine a fair split of money. For example, Sadaf and Dan shared a babysitting job one week and made $125. Sadaf baby-sat for 10 hours, and then Dan baby-sat for 15 hours. They can use bars to determine a fair way to split the money. Note that the ratio of 10 hours : 15 hours is a 2 : 3 ratio. They form the proportion $\frac{10\text{ hours}}{15\text{ hours}} = \frac{2\text{ parts}}{3\text{ parts}}$.

5 parts total (25 hours total)	
Sadaf – 2 parts 10 hours	Dan – 3 parts 15 hours
Sadaf $50	Dan $75
$125 ($25 per part or $5 per hour)	

Each part is $25, so Sadaf should get $50 for her two parts and Dan should get $75 for his 3 parts.

- Tables are also useful for proportions and ratios. For example, if a punch recipe calls for 2 cups of orange juice for every 3 cups of pineapple juice, the following table could be used to scale up the recipe for a greater number of servings.

Cups of Orange Juice	0	2	4	6	8	10	12	14	16	18	n
Cups of Pineapple Juice	0	3	6	9	12	15	18	21	24	27	$1.5n$
Total Cups of Punch	0	5	10	15	20	25	30	35	40	45	$2.5n$

This chart can be used to answer many types of questions. For example, you could find the number of cups of pineapple juice that are needed for n cups of orange juice. You could also find the total number of cups you would have if you had 8 more cups of pineapple juice than orange juice.

Unit Prices and Best Buys

- A unit price is the cost for one item or for one amount, such as one pound. Unit prices can be used to determine the best buy given several choices. Dividing the cost by the number of items or the amount, such as 3 pounds, gives the price for one item or one amount.
- An alternate method is to find the amount of an item per $1 spent. The following table shows both methods for comparing the best buy for grapes from three different stores.

Store	Fresh Produce	Green Grocers	Farmers Market
Price	3 pounds for $5	4 pounds for $6	5 pounds for $8
Unit Price	$1.67 per pound	$1.50 per pound	$1.60 per pound
Pounds per $1	0.60 pound	0.67 pound	0.625 pound

By either method, the Green Grocer has the best price for grapes.

MATHEMATICALLY SPEAKING

Do you know what these mathematical terms mean?

- concentration
- equivalent ratios
- part-to-part
- part-to-whole
- population density
- profit
- proportion
- ratio
- scaling down
- scaling up
- simplest form
- unit price

Study Guide

Using Proportional Reasoning

Part 1. What did you learn?

1. Jamie is a member of her school's Student Council. She noticed that there are 14 girls and 21 boys on the Student Council. Use this information to complete the tasks below.

   a. Write the ratio of the number of girls to the number of boys using a colon.

   b. Write the ratio of the number of girls to the number of boys using a fraction in simplest terms. Label each quantity.

   c. Write the ratio of the number of girls to the total number of students using a fraction in simplest terms. Label each quantity.

   d. Describe the relationship between the number of girls and the number of boys using the phrase "times as many."

2. The populations of Alaska and Vermont are about the same, but the area of Alaska is much larger than the area of Vermont. Based on this information, is the population density of Alaska greater than or less than the population density of Vermont? How do you know?

3. Abe, Beth, Cy and Dagmar wanted to know if their ear length to face length ratios were equivalent to the ratio 1 to 3 that Leonardo da Vinci used in his art. (The length of a man's ear to the length of his face is 1 to 3.) Determine if each student's ear length to face length ratio is equivalent to da Vinci's 1 to 3 ratio using the methods that you learned in this section. Show your work.

   a. Abe: "My ear length is 2.5 inches and my face length is 7.5 inches."

   b. Beth: "My face is three times as long as my ear."

   c. Cy: "The ratio of my ear length to face length is 0.3."

   d. Dagmar: "My ear length is 2 inches and my face length is $\frac{2}{3}$ of a foot."

4. The chart below contains information about the student populations (rounded to the nearest thousand) and campus areas (rounded to the nearest ten) of several universities in the United States. Use the information provided in Column A to choose the best estimate of the population density of that university in Column B.

Column A	Column B
a. Ohio State University Enrollment—54,000 students Area of main campus—1,760 acres	**i.** 300 students per acre
b. Northeastern University Enrollment—21,000 students Area of main campus—70 acres	**ii.** 90 students per acre
c. Harvard University Enrollment—20,000 students Area of main campus—380 acres	**iii.** 30 students per acre
d. UCLA Enrollment—38,000 Area of main campus—420 acres	**iv.** 50 students per acre

5. Nimah makes homemade play dough using flour, warm water, salt and vegetable oil. She often makes more than one batch.

   a. Copy and complete the chart showing the amounts of ingredients that Nimah needs for one or more batches.

   b. What is the ratio of flour to water expressed in simplest form using only whole numbers?

   c. What is the ratio of salt to vegetable oil expressed in simplest form using only whole numbers?

Ingredients	1 batch	2 batches	5 batches	10 batches
flour			10 cups	
water		$2\frac{1}{3}$ cups		
salt	$\frac{3}{4}$ cup			
vegetable oil				15 tbsp.

6. Clare bought gasoline at three different gas stations. She wants to know which gas station offers the best buy.

Gas Station	Number of Gallons	Number of Dollars
Station A	4	10
Station B	3	15
Station C	6	20

a. Compare the prices by scaling up ratios so that the number of gallons being compared is the same.

b. Compare the prices by scaling up ratios so that the number of dollars being compared is the same.

c. Which station has the best buy on gasoline?

7. Elena recycles plastic and glass containers at her local recycling center. Last month, she recycled 5 plastic containers for every 2 glass containers. She recycled a total of 49 plastic and glass containers. Use a bar diagram to find the number of plastic and glass containers Elena recycled.

8. Gina is making grapefruit juice by adding water to grapefruit juice concentrate. She found the following two recipes.

- Recipe 1: Mix 2 parts grapefruit juice concentrate to 3 parts water.
- Recipe 2: Mix 3 parts grapefruit juice concentrate to 5 parts water.

Which recipe has the greater grapefruit juice concentrate-to-water ratio? Show or explain how you got your answer.

9. Johan is comparing prices of three different but comparable brands of soap. He wants to know which of the three brands is the best buy.

Brand A: 4 bars for $5.00

Brand B: 3 bars for $4.50

Brand C: 6 bars for $6.00

Determine the best buy of the three brands of soap by finding a unit price for each brand of soap.

Part 2. What went wrong?

10. Doris was asked the following question on a recent quiz.

> Which brand of granola is the better buy?
>
> Brand A: 12 ounces for \$2.40
>
> Brand B: 16 ounce for \$3.40

Doris wrote, "The 16-ounce box of granola is the better buy because you get another 4 ounces for only one more dollar."

Doris's answer was marked wrong. Why? How would you explain to Doris why the 12-ounce box is the better buy?

11. The Student Council in Chad's school conducted a survey to determine which sport students wanted to play on field day. The Council reported that "Students prefer kickball to basketball by a ratio of 3 to 2." Chad said, "I'm surprised that they only surveyed 5 people." What is wrong with Chad's reasoning? How could you help Chad interpret the Council's statement correctly?

12. Tabitha was asked the following question on a recent quiz.

> There are 2 snowboarders for every 6 skiers on a ski slope. There are a total of 24 people on the ski slope. How many snowboarders are on the slope?

Tabitha used the proportion below to answer the question.

$$\frac{2}{6} = \frac{x}{24}$$

$$x = 8$$

Then, she wrote, "There are 8 snowboarders on the slope."

Tabitha's answer was marked wrong. What did Tabitha do wrong? How could you help her answer the question correctly?

Analyzing Change

In this section, you will continue to think like a mathematician as you analyze changes in the growth of plants and animals, in prices as the number of items you purchase increases and in your location as you move. You will also explore how coordinate graphs can be used to analyze change. You will explore this idea further when you study algebra and calculus.

Growing, Growing

Bamboo is a fast-growing type of grass. This table shows the growth of bamboo measured during the month of April in Alabama.

Date	April 2	April 9	April 12	April 13	April 22	April 30
Height	1'	3'	6'	10'	22'	30'

1. Did the bamboo grow at the same rate all month? How do you know?
2. Between April 12 and April 13, how many feet did the bamboo grow? What is the ratio of this growth to its height on April 12?
3. Giant kelp can grow 2 feet in one day. What else would you need to know to find whether the ratio of its growth to its initial length is more or less than it is for the bamboo?
4. A kudzu vine can grow 30 centimeters in one day. If a kudzu vine that is 25 centimeters long grows to 55 centimeters in one day, what is the ratio of its growth to its starting length? Compare this ratio to the growth of the bamboo between April 12 and April 13. Explain without using computation.

Comparing Rates

MATHEMATICALLY SPEAKING

- rate

A rate is a type of ratio that compares numbers with different units. A rate usually represents a change over time, distance or amount, such as the number of inches grown per day or the number of miles traveled per hour.

When a rate is constant, you can use proportions to determine how quantities such as time, distance or amounts change. For example, if you charge \$4.00 per hour to baby-sit, your babysitting rate is constant. It can be written as \$4.00 : 1 hour or $\frac{4 \text{ dollars}}{1 \text{ hour}}$.

Your rate could also be written as $\frac{1 \text{ hour}}{4 \text{ dollars}}$, $\frac{1}{4}$ hour per dollar, or $\frac{1}{4}$ hour : 1 dollar. So, this means that you would earn \$4.00 per hour or that you would work $\frac{1}{4}$ hour per every dollar earned. This rate stays the same whether you baby-sit for 1 hour or 10 hours.

To determine your earnings, set up the proportion $\frac{4}{1} = \frac{d}{h}$, where d is the amount in dollars you earn for babysitting for h hours. As the number of hours changes, so does the amount you earn. You can rewrite this proportion as the equation $4h = d$. If you baby-sit for 10 hours, you earn ten times as much as you would earn in 1 hour: If $\frac{4}{1} = \frac{d}{10}$, then $40 = d$. You would earn \$40.

1. Name three rates in the sentence below. Write each rate in at least two different ways. Be sure to include all labels in your rates.

   A car that can travel 25 miles per gallon of gas is moving at 45 miles per hour using gas that costs \$5.00 per gallon.

2. Did the bamboo in the Start It Off grow at a constant rate? How do you know?

3. A giant panda eats about 40 pounds of bamboo every day.

   a) At this rate, how many pounds of bamboo will a giant panda eat in 1 week?

   b) If p is the total number of pounds of bamboo a panda can eat in n days, write an equation that shows how p is related to n.

   c) How long would it take one panda to eat 1 ton of bamboo?

   d) About how many tons of bamboo would a pair of giant pandas eat over a year?

   e) A panda can live up to 35 years. How many tons of bamboo would one panda eat over 35 years?

   f) A giant panda weighs about 220 pounds and eats about 40 pounds of food a day. If a 150-pound woman ate the same ratio of food to body weight each day as a panda, how much would she eat?

   g) Giant pandas eat bamboo for about 14 hours per day. About how long does it take a giant panda to eat 1 pound of bamboo?

   h) If Tuan Tuan, a giant panda, eats about 1 pound of bamboo every 20 minutes and another giant panda, Yuan Yuan, eats about 1 pound every 30 minutes, does either panda eat 40 pounds in 14 hours? Which panda eats more? How much more? Compare the rate of days per pound of bamboo to the rate of pounds per day.

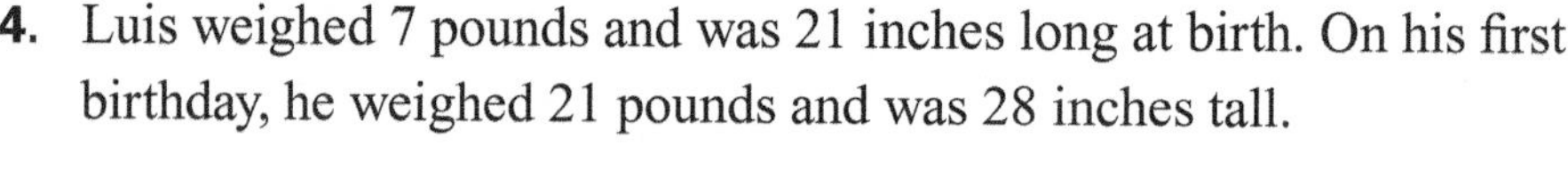

4. Luis weighed 7 pounds and was 21 inches long at birth. On his first birthday, he weighed 21 pounds and was 28 inches tall.

   a) If he continued to grow at this same rate, how much would he weigh and how tall would he be on his second birthday? On his third birthday? Show your work.

   b) Luis actually weighed 27 pounds and was 34 inches tall on his second birthday. Was his rate of change in height and weight greater or less in his second year than in his first year? Explain.

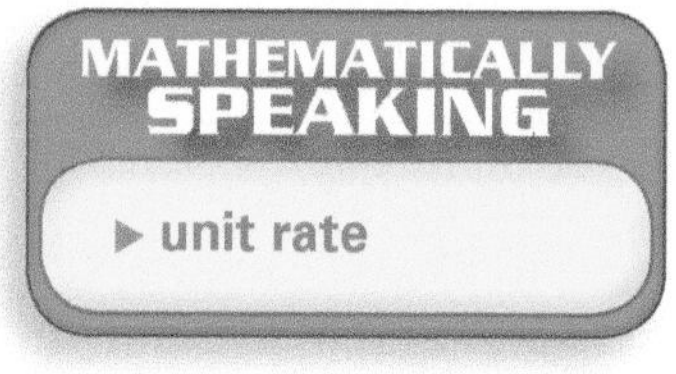

A unit rate compares one quantity to a single unit, such as 1 hour, 1 gallon or 1 year. The unit prices that you found in the previous lesson are unit rates. If you know that a train travels 300 miles in 5 hours, you could divide 300 miles by 5 hours to find a unit rate of 60 miles per hour. This can be written as the proportion:

$$\frac{300 \text{ miles}}{5 \text{ hours}} = \frac{60 \text{ miles}}{1 \text{ hour}}.$$

If you want to find the number of hours per mile instead of miles per hour, you could divide 5 hours by 300 miles to find an equivalent ratio of $\frac{1}{60}$ hour per mile. This can be written as:

$$\frac{5 \text{ hours}}{300 \text{ miles}} = \frac{1 \text{ hour}}{60 \text{ miles}} = \frac{\frac{1}{60} \text{ hour}}{1 \text{ mile}} = \frac{1 \text{ minute}}{1 \text{ mile}}.$$

Since $\frac{1}{60}$ hour is a minute, the average rate of the train is 1 minute per mile.

5. Bamboo can grow 21 feet in two weeks. Even though it does not grow the same amount each day, you can find an average unit rate. What is the average unit rate in feet per day for the amount this bamboo grew over these two weeks?

6. Compare the growth rate of bamboo that grows 21 feet in 2 weeks to the growth rate of kudzu that grows 30 inches in 3 days.

   a) At these rates, which would grow more in one month? How much more?

   b) Did you use unit rate to find this? Explain.

7. One bamboo plant grew for 4 days at an average rate of 12 inches per day. It then grew for 3 days at an average rate of 18 inches per day.

   a) How many total inches did it grow in the week?

   b) What was the average growth rate in inches per day for the seven days? Write your answer as a unit rate written in fraction form with 1 day in the denominator.

   c) What is its average growth rate in number of days (or hours) per inch?

Wrap It Up

MATHEMATICALLY SPEAKING

- rate
- unit rate

In 2005, a team from the University of Michigan traveled 2,500 miles in 54 hours in a solar-powered car. In 1995, Axel Fehlau traveled 635 miles in 24 hours in a human-powered vehicle. Talk to a partner about how you can compare the average speed of the solar car to the average speed of the human-powered vehicle using unit rates. What was the average unit rate of each in miles per hour? What was the average unit rate of each in hours per mile? How can you use each of these rates to find which vehicle had the faster rate?

LESSON 2.1 SECTION 2

On Your Own

Write About It

1. Car A can travel 990 miles on 22 gallons of gas. Car B can travel 525 miles on 15 gallons of gas.

   a) Find the average unit rate for each car in miles per gallon. Explain how you would use these unit rates to decide which car can travel farther on the same amount of gas.

   b) Find the average unit rate for each in gallons per mile. How can you use these unit rates to decide which car can travel further on the same amount of gas?

   c) Compare using miles per gallon to gallons per mile when deciding which car can travel farther on the same amount of gas.

2. A great white shark swam 6,800 miles in 99 days.

   a) Write this as an average unit rate in miles per day.

   b) Write this as an average unit rate in miles per hour.

   c) Write this as an average unit rate in hours per mile.

   d) At this rate, how many days would it take for the shark to swim 1,000 miles? Explain your method.

3. A sloth can travel a maximum of 5 feet per hour on land.

   a) Write this rate in miles per hour. Show your work.

   b) How long would it take the sloth to travel 1 foot? Write this as a unit rate both of hours per foot and of minutes per foot.

4. Ashrita Furman set a world record by traveling 37 kilometers on a pogo stick in $12\frac{1}{2}$ hours. What was his average rate in kilometers per hour?

5. Ashrita Furman also set a world record for walking with a milk bottle balanced on his head. He walked 130 kilometers in $23\frac{1}{2}$ hours.

   a) What was his average rate in kilometers per hour?

   b) How did this compare to his rate on a pogo stick?

6. Mr. Furman also holds the world record for the fastest 10-kilometer sack race, which he completed in $1\frac{1}{2}$ hours.

   a) Estimate whether his rate in kilometers per hour for the sack race was faster or slower than his rate for walking with a milk bottle on his head. Explain.

   b) If he could complete the 10-kilometer sack race at the same rate as he walked with a milk bottle balanced on his head, how long would the race take? Explain.

7. Maribel typed 225 words in five minutes.

   a) What was her average rate in words per minute?

   b) At this rate, how long would it take to type 2,000 words?

   c) What was Maribel's average rate in minutes per word?

8. Alan drove 60 miles in $1\frac{1}{2}$ hours. At this rate, how long would it take to drive another 40 miles? Show your work.

9. Aiden charges $4.50 per hour to baby-sit. How much should he charge if he baby-sits from 6 pm to 11:30 pm?

10. Mr. White drove 150 miles from his home to his son's home at an average speed of 60 miles per hour. He arrived at his son's home at 5 pm. What time did Mr. White start his trip?

11. Cashews are $6.50 per pound. If you spent $1.00, what part of a pound of cashews could you buy?

12. How would you compare two drivers' speeds if you knew they each drove for 4 hours? How would you compare their speeds if you knew they each drove for 50 miles?

13. If your heart beats 33 times in 15 seconds, what is your heart rate in beats per minute?

14. Mrs. deSilva drove for 3 hours at an average rate of 50 miles per hour. She then drove for 2 more hours at an average rate of 60 miles per hour.

    a) How many miles did Mrs. deSilva drive in these 5 hours?

    b) What was Mrs. deSilva's average rate for the entire trip in miles per hour?

    c) What was Mrs. deSilva's average rate in hours per mile?

On Your Own

15. Zoey drove by mile markers on the highway. At 2:10 pm, she passed a marker that read "Mile 47." At 2:30, she passed a marker that read "Mile 65." What was the average speed in miles per hour?

16. A police helicopter followed a car for $\frac{1}{5}$ mile for 10 seconds. How fast was the car traveling in miles per hour?

17. The Browns have a large SUV that can travel 10 miles per gallon of gas and a small car that can travel 25 miles per gallon of gas. They drive each vehicle about 5,000 miles per year. To spend less money on gas, they can either trade their SUV for one that can travel 20 miles per gallon of gas or trade their car for one that can travel 50 miles per gallon of gas. With which trade would save them more money each year? Explain.

18. The distance from Fort Thomas to Alexandria is about 11 miles (to the nearest mile). Which of these could be the actual distance?

A. 10.95 miles

B. 11.56 miles

C. 10.095 miles

D. 10.495 miles

19. Twenty-five copies of the same book are stacked together. If the stack is 18" high, what is the thickness of each book?

20. Write equivalent amounts for each of the following:

a) 24 ounces, in pounds and ounces

b) 18 cups, in quarts

c) 49 feet, in yards

d) 2,000 yards, in miles and feet

e) 5,400 pounds, in tons

21. Jordyn bought 2.25 pounds of cheese. Leah bought 35 ounces of cheese. The cheese cost $4.00 per pound.

a) Who bought more cheese? How much more?

b) What did each person pay for her cheese?

22. One-fourth of a pitcher holds six cups. How much does $\frac{1}{8}$ of the same pitcher hold?

LESSON 2.2 Constant Change

As you've seen, some things do not change at a constant rate while other things have a constant rate of change. In the last lesson, you learned to use unit rates or ratios to solve problems involving change. Many of these can also be solved using tables or proportions. In this lesson, you will continue to solve rate, ratio and proportion problems using a variety of methods.

Jennifer paid $0.90 in sales tax on a $15 purchase. At this rate, what is the sales tax for a $50 purchase? Be prepared to share your thinking.

Recycling Ratios

Many students are concerned about all the trash that the festival will generate. They want to recycle as much as possible. The following are a few of the uses for recycled 2-liter plastic bottles.

Number of Recycled Bottles	10	120	25	81
Number of Objects Made	2 large T-shirts	4 sleeping bags	Filler for 5 ski jackets	3 sweaters

Source: EPA Quest for Less: http://www.epa.gov/wastes/education/quest/index.htm

Mackenzie wants to know how many bottles must be recycled to make 11 sweaters. She has made the following table.

Number of Sweaters Made	3	6	9	1	2	11
Number of Recycled Bottles	81	162	243	27	54	297

1. Mackenzie used multiplication and the information about 3 sweaters to find the number of bottles needed for 6 and 9 sweaters.

   a) What operation do you think Mackenzie used with the information about 3 sweaters to find the number of bottles needed for 1 sweater?

   b) Why do you think Mackenzie wanted to find the number of bottles needed for 1 sweater after she had found the number of bottles needed for 9 sweaters?

   c) How do you think Mackenzie used the number of bottles needed for 9 sweaters and the number needed for 2 sweaters to find the number needed for 11 sweaters?

   d) Use Mackenzie's table to find the number of bottles needed to make:

   - 8 sweaters
   - 5 sweaters
   - 14 sweaters

Compare your answers to a partner's. Did you get the same answers? Did you use the same method?

2. **a)** Complete the following table to find the number of recycled bottles that would be needed to make 15 sleeping bags.

Number of Sleeping Bags Made	4	8				
Number of Recycled Bottles	120					

   b) Compare your table to a partner's. Did you get the same answer? Did you complete the table in the same way?

   c) Jake said that you could just find the number of bottles needed for 1 sleeping bag and then multiply. Use Jake's method to find the number of bottles needed for 15 sleeping bags.

   d) Compare Jake's method to Mackenzie's. Which method uses a unit rate? Which method do you prefer?

After much discussion about recycling, the refreshments committee has decided to sell water and juice at the festival. They will make a profit on the sales and then recycle the bottles. They plan to sell half-liter bottles of water for \$1.00 each and 12-ounce bottles of juice for \$1.25 each.

Their cost will be based on these ads. They plan to sell at least 200 bottles of water and 200 bottles of juice.

Water

2 packs of 24 half-liter bottles - \$7.20

1 pack of 12 half-liter bottles - \$2.00

3. Look at the ads above for the water and juice.

a) Which is the better buy for the water? Using your choice, what will the water cost per bottle?

b) How much profit will they make on each bottle of water?

c) Which is the better buy for the juice? Using your choice, what will the juice cost per bottle?

d) How much profit will they make on each bottle of juice?

4. Fill in this table to show the profit on bottles of water using the bottles that are the better buy.

Bottles Sold	0	25	50	75	100	125	150	175	200	225	250
Profit	0										

a) What patterns do you notice in the table?

b) Write an explicit rule for the profit (p) on water based on the number of bottles of water sold (w).

c) Make a similar table to show the profit on bottles of juice using the bottles that are the better buy. Write an explicit rule for the profit (p) on juice based on the number of bottles of juice sold (j).

d) If the refreshments committee sells 200 bottles of water and 200 bottles of juice, what will their total profit be?

e) Write an explicit rule for the total profit (p) based on the number of bottles of water sold (w) and the number of bottles of juice sold (j).

Five pounds of cheese cost $15.45.

a) Complete the table to find the cost of the 17 pounds of cheese.

Pounds of Cheese	0	5	10				
Cost	0	$15.45					

b) Talk to a partner about how you found the cost of 17 pounds of cheese. Did you get the same answer? Did you complete the table in the same way?

c) Use a unit price to determine the cost for 17 pounds of cheese. Compare this method to finding the price using the table.

LESSON 2.2 SECTION 2

On Your Own

Write About It

1. Five bushels of corn can be used to make 14 gallons of ethanol.

   a) Use the given information to complete the table.

Bushels of Corn	0	1	2	3	4	5	6
Gallons of Ethanol	0					14	

   b) Explain how you can write an explicit rule for the number of gallons of ethanol (g) that can be made from a given number of bushels of corn (b).

2. The refreshments committee plans to serve tacos. Four packages contain 32 taco shells.

   a) Copy and complete the table to find the number of taco shells in 25 packages.

Number of Packages	0	4	8				
Number of shells	0	32					

   b) If they plan to sell 240 tacos, how many packages should they buy?

   c) Write an explicit rule for the total number of taco shells (t) in a given number of packages (p).

3. A 2012 Dodge® Viper can travel about 266 miles on a full 18.5-gallon tank of gas. A 2012 Ford® Focus can travel about 340 miles on a full 13.5-gallon tank.

   a) Without computing, which car gets better mileage? Explain.

   b) Find the unit rate in miles per gallon for each vehicle. Show your work.

   c) Copy and complete the table to show the number of miles each car can travel for the given amount of gas.

Gallons of Gas	0	1	2	3	4	5	6
Dodge Viper Miles Traveled							
Ford Focus Miles Traveled							

d) Write an explicit rule for each car giving the number of miles (m) it will travel on a given number of gallons of gas (g).

e) How much farther could the Focus travel on a total of 20 gallons of gas than the Viper? Show your work.

4. Ten bushels of corn can make 330 pounds of sweetener.

a) Make a table to show the pounds of sweetener that you could make from 0, 1, 2, 3, 4 and 5 bushels.

b) Write a general rule for the pounds of sweetener (p) that can be produced from each bushel (b).

5. Recycling 350 pounds of newspaper can save about 3 trees.

a) Copy and complete the table to show how much newspaper must be recycled to save 25 trees.

Trees Saved	0	3	6				
Pounds of Recycled Newspaper	0	350					

b) Use a unit rate to determine the pounds of recycled newspaper needed to save 25 trees.

c) Compare the two methods. Did you get the same answer? Which method do you prefer? Explain.

6. In 2001, about a million aluminum beverage cans were recycled in the United States every eight minutes. Make a table to find the number of cans that were recycled every hour in the United States at this rate.

7. For the bake sale, cookies sell for $0.65 apiece, cakes for $8.00 apiece, and pies for $7.00 apiece. Copy and complete the table to show the amount collected for each number sold. Include a general rule for n items sold of each.

Number Sold	0	1	2	3	4	5	6	n
Cookie Income	0	$0.65						
Cake Income	0	$8.00						
Pie Income	0	$7.00						

8. Harry burns 75 calories for every 15 minutes that he walks.

a) How long must Harry walk to burn 450 calories?

b) How many calories can Harry burn in one hour?

c) Write a general rule for the number of calories burned (c) for the number of hours walked (h).

On Your Own

9. Five pies were sold for every 8 cakes sold. Pies were sold for \$7 and cakes were sold for \$8. A total of \$594 was collected. How many pies were sold?

10. Plot the following points on a coordinate grid.

    $A\,(4, 3)$ $B\,(2, 5)$ $C\,(6, 0)$ $D\,(-3, 1)$ $E\,(-4, -3)$ $F\,(1, -3)$

11. Order the following fractions from the least to the greatest: $\frac{7}{5}, \frac{3}{4}, \frac{3}{8}, \frac{2}{3}, \frac{6}{5}$.

Use this pictograph to answer Questions 12–14.

Class	Number of Books Read
Ms. White	[book] [book] [book] [book]
Mr. Johnson	[book] [book] [book] [half book]
Mr. Sholy	[book] [book] [book] [book] [book]
Ms. Nunez	[book] [book] [book] [book] [book] [half book]

Key [book] = 20 Books

12. How many books total did the four classes read?

13. How many more books did Ms. Nunez's class read than Ms. White's class?

14. Which classes read more: the classes with male teachers or the classes with female teachers? How many more books did those classes read?

LESSON 2.3

Graphing Change

You have solved problems involving ratios and rates by using proportions and tables. In this lesson, you will use coordinate graphs to solve this type of problem.

Start It Off

Use the double line graph below to answer the following questions about recycling PET (polyethylene terephthalate) bottles.

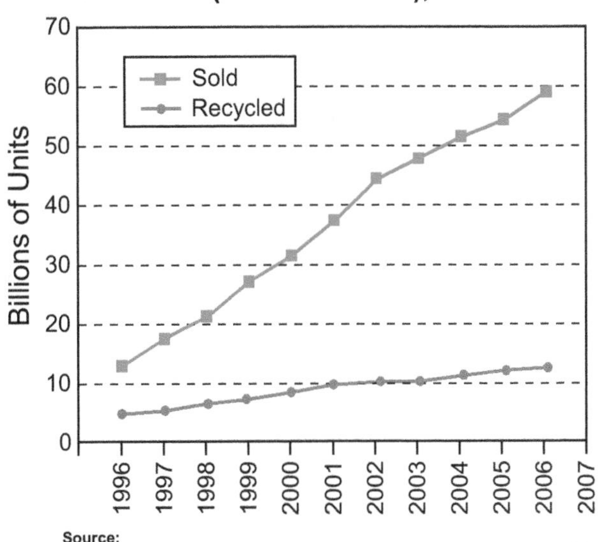

Source:
CRI data derived from American Plastics Council, National Association of PET Container Resources. Includes dairy.© *Container Recycling Institute, 2(*

1. Approximate the ratio of the number of PET bottles sold in 2006 to the number recycled in 2006.
2. Approximate the ratio of the number of PET bottles sold in 1996 to the number recycled in 1996.
3. Denise said that people recycled more in 2006 than in 1996 since they recycled about 7 billion more PET bottles in 2006 than in 1996. Talk to a partner about whether you agree with Denise.

Popular Punch

Jacquie plans to make her favorite punch for the festival. The recipe calls for 2 cups of sherbet for every 4 cups of lemon-lime drink.

1. a) Copy and complete the table to show how many cups of lemon-lime drink she would need for different amounts of sherbet.

Cups of Sherbet	0	1	2	3	4	5	6
Cups of Lemon-Lime Drink	0		4				

b) If Jacquie uses a gallon of lemon-lime drink, how much sherbet should she use?

c) If Jacquie uses 4 quarts of sherbet, how much lemon-lime drink should she use?

d) Add a row to your table that shows the ratios of cups of sherbet to cups of lemon-lime drink in simplest form. What do you notice?

Cups of Sherbet	0	1	2	3	4	5	6
Cups of Lemon-Lime Drink	0		4				
$\frac{\text{Cups of Sherbet}}{\text{Cups of Lemon-Lime Drink}}$			$\frac{2}{4} = \frac{1}{2}$				

e) Write an explicit rule for the number of cups of lemon-lime drink for each cup of sherbet.

MATHEMATICALLY SPEAKING
- scatter plot

Jacquie plotted points on a coordinate graph to show the relationship between the numbers of cups of each ingredient. A graph in which you plot points but do not connect them is called a scatter plot. When the dots are connected with a line, it is called a line graph.

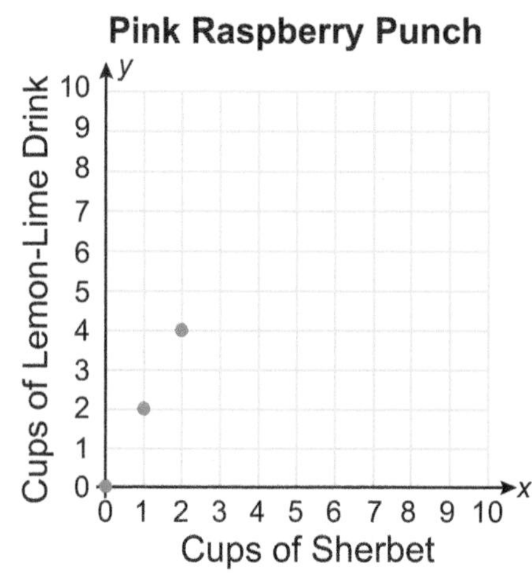

2. Look at the graph.

a) What do the points represent?

b) Plot the other points from your table.

c) Should this be a scatter plot or a line graph? Why? If you connected the points, would they all lie on the same line? How does this relate to the ratio of sherbet to lemon-lime drink for each of your points?

3. Jacquie found that she could buy a gallon of sherbet for $5.00.

a) Copy and complete the table to show what you would pay for different amounts of sherbet at this price.

Gallons of Sherbet	0	1	2	3	4	5	6
Price	0	$5.00					

b) Add a row to your table that shows the ratio of price of sherbet : gallons of sherbet in simplest form. What do you notice?

Gallons of Sherbet	0	1	2	3	4	5	6
Price	0	$5.00					
$\frac{\text{Price of Sherbet}}{\text{Gallons of Sherbet}}$	———	$\frac{5}{1}$					

c) Graph the points from your table on a graph similar to this.

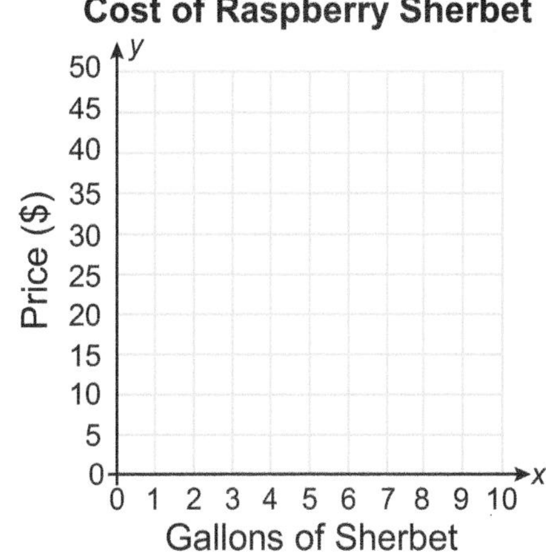

d) Should you connect the points on your graph? Why or why not? If you connected the points, would they all lie on the same line?

e) How might you use your graph to find the cost for 8 gallons? For 10 gallons?

f) At the rate of $5.00 per gallon, what should $\frac{1}{2}$ gallon of sherbet cost? Locate this point on your graph. Would this point lie on the same line as the others?

g) The cost of a half-gallon container of sherbet is actually $3. Locate this point on your graph. Does it lie on the same line as the others? Why or why not?

4. Mr. Hanson's class is making soap crayons to sell at the International Festival. To make 1 set of 20 crayons, they use 1 cup of soap flakes, 2 tablespoons of hot water and a drop of food coloring.

   a) Make a table to show the number of cups of soap flakes and tablespoons of hot water needed for 0, 1, 2, 3, 4 and 5 sets of 20 crayons.

   b) Include a row on your table that lists the ratio of the cups of soap flakes to tablespoons of hot water needed for each set. Write each ratio in simplest form.

   c) Graph the points from your table. Show the cups of soap flakes on the x-axis and the tablespoons of hot water on the y-axis. Include a title. What scale should you use on each axis? Should you connect the points? Explain.

   d) Talk to a partner about how you can use the graph to find how much hot water you should use with $1\frac{1}{2}$ cups of soap flakes. How many crayons would this make?

   e) How might you use your graph to find the number of tablespoons of hot water you should use with 8 cups of soap flakes?

   f) Janelle has a recipe for crayons that uses $1\frac{3}{4}$ cups of soap flakes for each $\frac{1}{4}$ cup of hot water. Locate this point on your graph. Is this ratio of soap flakes to hot water the same as the ratio of soap flakes to hot water for the other points on your graph? Explain.

See page 150

Wrap It Up

MATHEMATICALLY SPEAKING

▶ scatter plot

Mr. Jackson drove the following distances in the times given.

Miles Driven	75	25	120	50	250	125
Time	$1\frac{1}{2}$ hours	30 minutes	2 hours	1 hour	5 hours	2.5 hours

a) Copy the table and add a row for the ratios of miles to hours in simplest form.

b) Which point would you not expect to lie on the same line as the others when graphed? Talk to a partner about why this point is different. If you plot the other points on a graph with the time in hours on the *x*-axis and the miles driven on the *y*-axis, will this point lie above or below the line the others are on?

c) Create the graph. Was your prediction correct? Talk to your partner about what you noticed. How is this related to proportions and equivalent ratios?

LESSON 2.3 SECTION 2

On Your Own

1. Three pounds of cherries cost $13.50

   a) Find the price for 1 pound of cherries.

   b) Explain how to use the unit price to show the relationship between the price of cherries and the number of pounds purchased. Illustrate your description using a table and a graph. Should you connect the points on the graph?

   c) Cynthia bought 5 pounds of cherries for $20. Will this point lie on your line? Why or why not?

2. One cup of corn flakes has 2 grams of sugar.

   a) Create a table showing the amount of sugar in 0, 1, 2, 3, 4 and 5 cups of corn flakes.

   b) Graph this relationship with cups of corn flakes on the x-axis and grams of sugar on the y-axis. Should you connect the points?

   c) There are 3 grams of sugar in $1\frac{1}{3}$ cups of another cereal. Will this point lie on your line? Explain.

3. Waste paper from the United States and Europe is shipped to China to be recycled. The average person in the United States uses about 700 pounds of paper per year.

   a) Copy and complete this table.

Number of People	0	10	20	30	40	50
Average Weight of Used Paper in Tons per Year	0					

   b) Add a row to the table for the ratios of the number of people to the average weight of used paper in tons in simplest form. What do you notice?

   c) Predict the shape of the graph of these points if you plot the number of people on the x-axis and the average weight of used paper per year on the y-axis.

   d) Construct the graph.

e) Use the graph to find the number of tons of paper that you would expect 15 people in the United States to use in a year.

f) The average person outside the United States uses about 110 pounds of paper. If you plot a point showing the average number of pounds of paper used by 10 people outside the United States, will it lie on the same line as the other points? Explain.

4. A 2012 Toyota™ Prius travels 576 miles on 12 gallons of gas. A 2012 Honda™ Civic Hybrid travels 600 miles on 15 gallons of gas.

a) Find the average number of miles each car can travel on 1 gallon of gas.

b) Make a table showing the average number of miles each car would travel on 0, 1, 2, 3, 4 and 5 gallons.

c) Graph the points for the Toyota™ Prius with the number of gallons on the x-axis and the number of miles it can travel on the y-axis. Should all these points lie on the same line? Explain.

d) If you were to add the points for the Civic Hybrid on this graph, do you think that they would be above or below the points for the Prius? Why?

e) Graph the points and check your prediction.

LESSON 2.3 SECTION 2

On Your Own

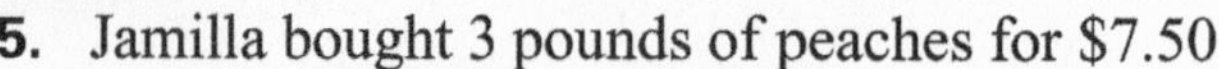

5. Jamilla bought 3 pounds of peaches for \$7.50.

a) At this price, make a table showing the cost of 0, 3, 6, 9, 12 and 15 pounds of peaches.

b) Graph your points with the number of pounds of peaches on the *x*-axis and the price on the *y*-axis.

c) Does it make sense to connect these points? Why or why not? If you did connect these points, would they all lie on the same line?

d) At this rate, what is the price of $4\frac{1}{2}$ pounds of peaches? Explain how you can use the graph to find this.

e) What is the unit price for 1 pound of peaches?

f) Write an equation for the total cost (c) of any number (n) of pounds of peaches.

g) What is the cost of 18 pounds of peaches? Explain how you can find this using the graph and how you can find it using your equation.

6. At the beginning of this section, you saw this table showing the growth of bamboo.

Date	April 2	April 9	April 12	April 13	April 22
Height	1'	3'	6'	10'	22'

a) Plot the points on a coordinate grid similar to this one.

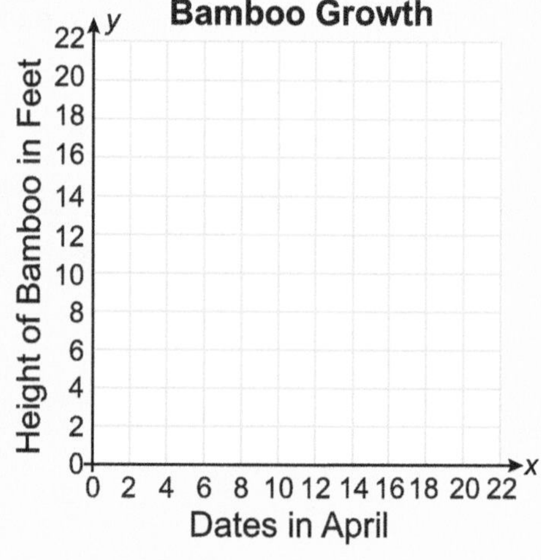

b) Does it make sense to connect the points on the graph? Do all the points lie on the same line? Why or why not?

7. Choose one of the tables you made in Lesson 2.2 and graph the points from your table. Do all the points lie on the same line? Why or why not?

8. The formula for the area of a circle is $A = \pi r^2$. You may use 3.14 as an approximation of pi.

   a) Make a table of the areas of circles with a radius of 0, 1, 2, 3, 4 and 5 inches.

   b) If you graph these points on a grid with the length of the radius on the x-axis and the area on the y-axis, will all the points lie on the same straight line? Why or why not?

   c) Is the relationship between the radius and the area of a circle proportional?

   d) Graph the points and check your prediction. What is the shape of your graph?

9. Locate the following points on the number line: $\frac{17}{5}, \frac{3}{7}, \frac{4}{8}, \frac{2}{3}, \frac{6}{5}$.

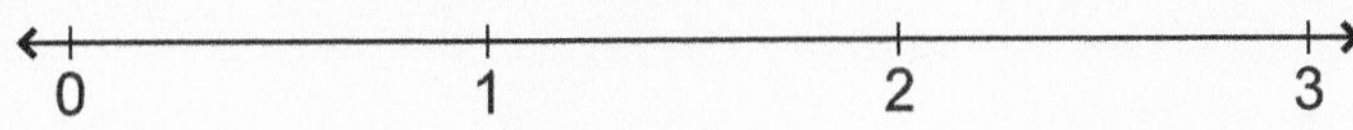

10. Which is larger: 3^4 or 4^3? Explain.

11. Solve for n. Show your work.

    a) $14 + n = 65 - 8$

    b) $15.9 - 4.35 = n + 10$

    c) $8 \cdot (5 - 2) - 4 + 1 \cdot 3 = n$

12. You have a rectangular garden with an area of 36 square feet and a width of 4 feet.

    a) What is the length of your garden?

    b) What is the perimeter of your garden?

13. Write as a decimal: $87 + \frac{4}{1{,}000} + \frac{7}{10}$.

Sum It Up

In this section, you used rates, ratios and proportions to analyze change in situations ranging from growth of plants to the uses of recycled materials.

Change and Rates

- Change can be described using addition and subtraction or multiplication and division. For example, if you were 55 inches tall on your tenth birthday and 60 inches tall on your twelfth birthday, you could use addition or subtraction to show that your height had changed by 5 inches. Using multiplication or division and the ratio of the 5 inches you grew to your height of 55 inches tall on your tenth birthday, you can say the ratio of the growth to your original height was $5:55$ or $1:11$. The growth was $\frac{1}{11}$ of your original height. If your little brother also grew 5 inches in those 2 years from 30 inches to 35 inches, he grew $\frac{5}{30}$ or $\frac{1}{6}$ of his original height.
- Rates compare two quantities with different units, such as distance and time or gallons and miles.
- A unit rate indicates the number of units of one quantity related to a single unit of another, such as miles per gallon or feet per second. A unit rate is equivalent to the original rate. For example, if a car travels 150 miles on 5 gallons of gas, the unit rate is $150 \div 5$ or 30 miles per gallon $\left(\frac{150 \text{ miles}}{5 \text{ gallons}} = \frac{30 \text{ miles}}{1 \text{ gallon}}\right)$. You could also say that it would take $5 \div 150$ or $\frac{1}{30}$ gallon to travel 1 mile $\left(\frac{5 \text{ gallons}}{150 \text{ miles}} = \frac{\frac{1}{30} \text{ gallon}}{1 \text{ mile}}\right)$.

Constant Change

- Rates are often used to describe a proportional relationship where the rate is constant. For example, if a car gets an average of 30 miles per gallon of gas, with 1 gallon you can travel 30 miles, with 2 gallons you can travel 60 miles, with 3 gallons you can travel 90 miles, and so on. You can use a table to show this relationship.

Gallons of Gas	0	1	2	3	4	5	n
Miles Driven	0	30	60	90	120	150	$30n$

- When you identify a proportional relationship, you can use the constant rate to write a formula to describe it. In this case, since miles per gallon is represented by 30 miles : 1 gallon, you might write the explicit rule $m = 30g$ to show that the number of miles (m) you can drive is equal to 30 times the number of gallons (g) of gas used.
- Coordinate graphs are useful for graphing how a quantity changes. This is often done by plotting points from a table. If there is a constant rate of change, the points will all lie on the same line. For the table above, the points on the corresponding graph can be connected because all the points on that line have meaning; you can drive part of a mile or use part of a gallon. Be careful not to connect points on a scatter plot if the values in between do not have meaning.

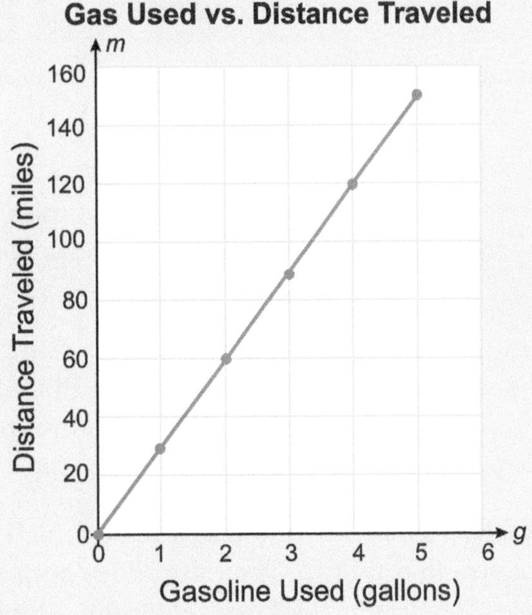

MATHEMATICALLY SPEAKING

Do you know what these mathematical terms mean?

- rate
- scatter plot
- unit rate

SECTION 2

Study Guide

Analyzing Change

Part 1. What did you learn?

1. Blank CDs are sold in packages. Three packages contain 18 blank CDs.

   a. Use a table to find the number of CDs in 24 packages.

   b. Use a table to find the number of packages needed for 90 CDs.

2. Miley kept track of how far she had run on a treadmill over certain time intervals, as shown in the chart below.

Minutes	6	24	30	72	84
Miles	0.5	2	3	6	7
Minutes Per Mile					

   a. Copy and complete the row that gives the ratio of minutes per miles in simplest form, with minutes and miles both written as whole numbers.

   b. If you were to graph Miley's data on a graph with number of minutes on the x-axis and number of miles on the y-axis, would all of the points fall in a straight line? Why or why not?

3. The Smithsons have two cars. They need to decide which car to drive on their upcoming road trip. Their two-door coupe can travel 300 miles on a 12-gallon tank of gas. Their four-door sedan can travel 320 miles on a 16-gallon tank of gas.

   a. Copy and complete the chart below.

	Two-Door Coupe	Four-Door Sedan
Miles Per Gallon		
Gallons Per Mile		

   b. Which car gets better gas mileage?

   c. Write an explicit rule for finding the number of gallons (g) needed to travel a given number of miles (m) in the Smithsons' two-door coupe.

   d. Write an explicit rule for finding the number of gallons (g) needed to travel a given number of miles (m) in the Smithsons' four-door sedan.

4. Another way to think about gas consumption in cars is to calculate a rate of dollars spent per mile. This rate determines the cost, in dollars, of traveling 1 mile in a car.

   a. If gas costs $3.20 per gallon, find the rate of dollars per mile for the two cars in Question 3. Use a calculator.

   b. Based on your answer from Part a, which car should the Smithsons drive on their road trip? Did you get the same answer as in Question 3b?

5. Rinaldo makes and sells tie-dyed T-shirts to raise money for his favorite charity. He spent $80 on supplies to make the T-shirts and will sell each T-shirt for $12.

   a. Copy and complete the following table to show the balance of the amount of money Rinaldo will have after selling each number of T-shirts.

   b. Plot the data from your table on a graph.

   c. Does it make sense to connect the points? Why or why not?

   d. What is the least number of T-shirts that Rinaldo must sell in order to earn back the $80 he spent on supplies?

T-Shirts Sold	0	1	2	3	4	5	6	7	8
Balance	−$80	−$68							

Part 2. What went wrong?

6. Heather was asked the following question on a recent multiple-choice quiz.

> Dom babysits his little cousin for $10 each hour. Which of the following expresses Dom's rate of hours per dollar?
>
> A. $\frac{1}{10}:1$ C. 1:60
>
> B. 10:1 D. 60:10

Heather chose letter B, but her answer was marked wrong. Why? How could you help Heather find the correct answer?

7. Tedy was asked the following question on a recent quiz.

> When Larry exercises, he drinks 6 ounces of water every 15 minutes to stay hydrated. If he plans to exercise for a total of 9 hours this week, how many ounces of water should he drink?

Tedy wrote, "Larry needs 54 ounces since $6 \cdot 9 = 54$." Tedy's answer was marked wrong. Why? How could you help Tedy find the correct answer?

Using Data to Make Comparisons

You live in an information age! Every time you turn around, you are bombarded with information, often referred to as data. Data are numbers or facts that describe things such as people or places. In this section, you will learn how to collect, organize, analyze, interpret and present data in order to answer statistical questions and to continue to plan for the International Festival.

LESSON 3.1 Describing Data

Start It Off

MATHEMATICALLY SPEAKING

- data
- numerical data
- categorical data

Data are often referred to as numerical data or categorical data. Examples of numerical data are numbers such as 3 siblings and measurements such as 18 centimeters. Categorical data are facts that include the specific name of a category such as the names of different sports or the names of different seasons.

1. Write two different questions you could ask everyone in your class that would have a number as an answer.
2. Write two different questions you could ask everyone in your class that would have a category for an answer. Data that can be placed in a category are colors, types of music, and foods.
3. Explain how numerical data and categorical data are similar and how they are different.

In this lesson you will start to consider and answer statistical questions. Statistical questions ask about sets of data. There are many ways we can describe data in order to answer questions!

Dot Plots

MATHEMATICALLY SPEAKING

- dot plot
- distribution of data
- gaps
- clusters
- range

In this digital age it is useful to be able to type essays and homework assignments for school quickly. Cutting down on typos in emails and texts helps to guarantee you are not misunderstood. A group of sixth-grade students took a one-week summer class to improve their keyboarding skills. At the start of the course they were given a keyboarding test. Below is a dot plot, also known as a line plot, showing their typing rate—the number of words they typed per minute with accuracy.

Summer Class Keyboarding Pre-Test

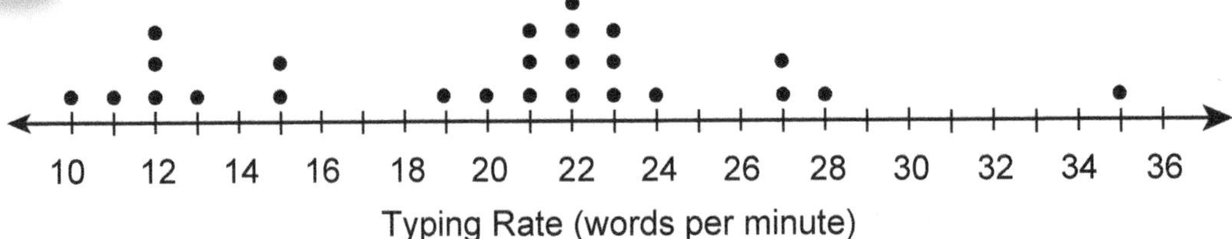

1. a) How many students took the summer keyboarding class?

   b) How is the total number of students determined from a dot plot?

Statisticians are interested in understanding how data can be used to answer questions. As a result, they look for ways to describe data sets using numbers and descriptors. One way to describe the spread of data, or distribution of data, is to give the range. The range is the difference between the maximum value and the minimum value. The range provides information on the spread of the data; it tells us how far apart the extreme data values are. Another way to describe the distribution of a data set is to look at the overall shape formed by gaps and clusters. Gaps are intervals of numbers for which there are no data values, and clusters are intervals where several data values are grouped close together.

2. Describe the distribution of the data for the sixth graders' keyboarding skills using the dot plot above. Be sure to include the range as well as information about the shape of the distribution.

3. Use your descriptions from Question 2 to answer this question: "At the start of the one-week course, how good were these sixth graders' keyboarding skills in terms of speed and accuracy?"

At the end of the week, the sixth graders took another timed keyboarding test that indicated the number of words they could type per minute with accuracy. These data are shown in the dot plot below.

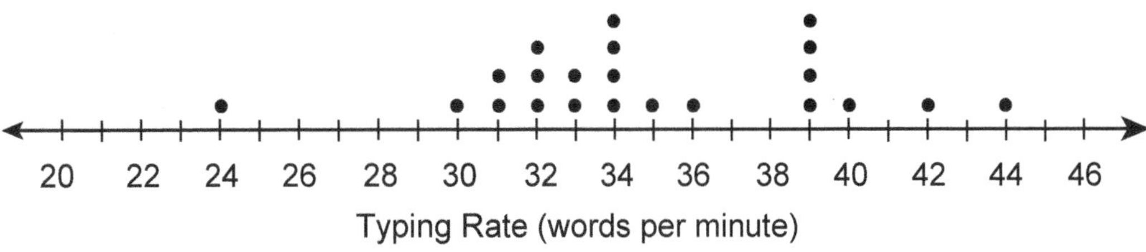

4. a) Describe the distribution of data in the dot plot at the end of the course.

   b) Compare the two distributions. What conclusions can you make?

5. Which of the following statements can be supported using the data from the two dot plots? If the statement cannot be supported, explain why.

   a) In the one-week course, the students all learned to type with both hands.

   b) The sixth graders were faster and more accurate at keyboarding after taking the course.

   c) More students started the course than finished the course.

   d) The range of the post-course data was 42 through 92.

   e) Students who took the course are able to type on a keyboard faster than other students.

6. Elyssa and Elmer were discussing how else they might describe the data set.

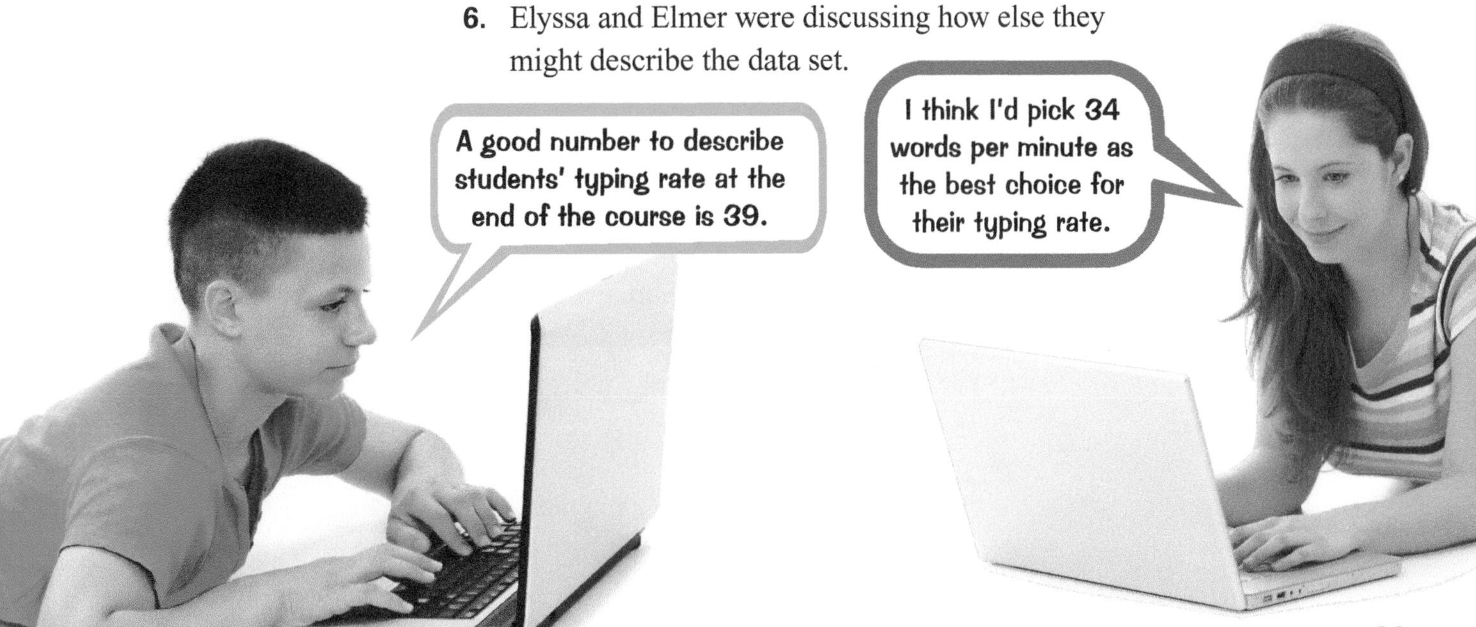

a) Which number do you think best describes the "typical" number of words per minute students could type?

b) Is there a different number that you think would better represent the students' typing rate at the end of the course? Explain.

MATHEMATICALLY SPEAKING

- measure of center
- median
- mean

When describing the distribution of data, you want to consider what is typical. Statisticians often use a number to summarize the numerical values in a set; this number is called a measure of center because it provides information about the data in the center! There are two different measures of center commonly used: the median and the mean.

Example

- The median is the number in the middle of the data set when the values are arranged from least to greatest. It divides the data set in half so that there are an equal number of data values below the median, or middle value, and an equal number of data values above the median.

  Example: The following set represents the number of computer games owned by a group of sixth graders: 14, 8, 10, 17, 23, 11 and 12.

  8, 10, 11, 12, 14, 17, 23 The median number of computer games owned by the students is 12.

- The mean is a number that describes the data set as if all values in the set were the same. It is sometimes called the "arithmetic average." You find the mean by adding all of the data values in a set together and dividing by the number of data items. Examine how the mean for the data set describing keyboarding rates after instruction was calculated.

The mean is

$$\frac{24+30+31+31+32+32+32+33+33+34+34+34+34+35+36+39+39+39+39+40+42+44}{22} = \frac{767}{22} \approx 34.9.$$

MATHEMATICALLY SPEAKING

- mode
- bimodal

You may have learned about the mode in other math classes. The mode helps us describe a data set but many statisticians do not consider it a measure of center. The mode is the most frequent data value. Sometimes there isn't a mode in a data set. In other data sets, there are two values that occur most frequently. These data sets are said to be bimodal, having two modes!

For example, the mode for the Summer Keyboarding Class Pre-Test data set is 22 words per minute, as this value occurs most frequently. The Post-Test data set is bimodal.

7. a) Determine the modes of the data set for keyboarding rates following instruction.

   b) Determine the median of the same data set.

   c) Compare the median and mean of the data set. How are these measures similar and different?

8. It seems like the two measures of center for a data set should be the exact same number, but they are not in this case. Why not?

Exploring Heights

The International Festival's planning committee is designing some games for the festival where the average heights of sixth-grade students is an important factor. Let's now use statistics to describe the height of the students in your classroom. With a partner measure both of your heights in inches. Write your heights on Post-it® notes and put them on the number line that your teacher has drawn on the board. The start of your dot plot using Post-it® notes might look similar to the plot below.

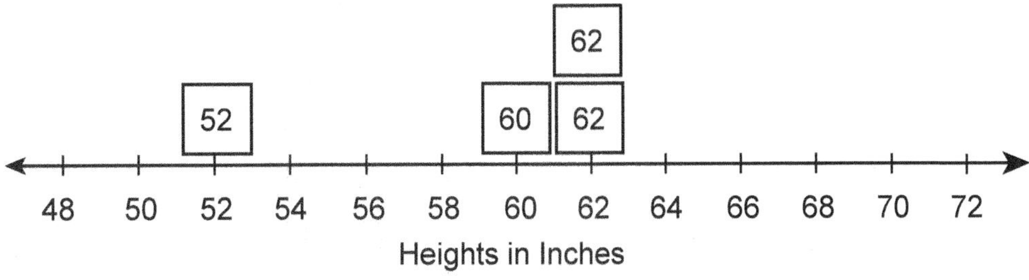

9. a) Describe the distribution of the height data for your class. How spread out are the values? Are there clusters or gaps? Don't forget the range.

   b) Determine the median of the data set. If there are an even number of data values, the median is found by averaging the two middle numbers (adding them and dividing by 2).

   c) Explain which measure of center you think best describes these data and determine this summary number.

   d) Write a sentence or two that tells someone about the heights of the students in your sixth-grade class.

   e) Do you think these data are representative of most sixth-grade classes? Why or why not?

Wrap It Up

Two features of data sets are important to examine: the distribution and the center. Share what you know about these features of a data set.

MATHEMATICALLY SPEAKING

- bimodal
- categorical data
- clusters
- data
- distribution of data
- dot plot
- gap
- mean
- measure of center
- median
- mode
- numerical data
- range

LESSON 3.1 SECTION 3

On Your Own

Write About It

1. Why do statisticians want to know about the spread of a data set and the center of a data set? Explain what these are, give an example of each, and then write about what they tell us.

2. As part of his science project, Mark tracked the depth of a stream each week. Here are his measurements in inches for 9 weeks in the spring.

   17 16 15 18 19 17 16 16 14

   a) What is the median of his data?

   b) Mark continued to take measurements into the summer. His next 4 measurements were 15, 12, 11 and 12. What is the new median?

   c) Give the range using all the measurements.

   d) Mark wrote the following about this data set: "The depth of the stream had a range of 11 inches to 19 inches. This may have to do with the changing amount of rain from spring to summer. On average, the stream has 15 to 17 inches of water in it." Rewrite these sentences to report on the range and measures of center.

3. Examine the dot plot showing the weight of cats owned by students at one school.

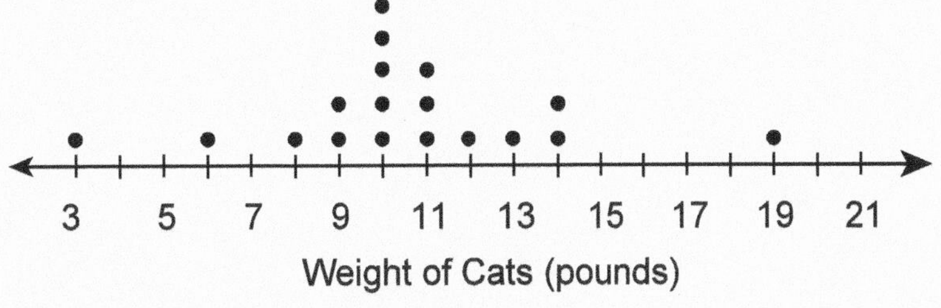

   a) How many cats were weighed?

   b) Describe the distribution of these data. Give a possible reason why a cat might have the minimum or maximum weight.

   c) What does the distribution tell you about the size of cats?

   d) How do you determine the median from a dot plot? Give the median.

   e) Is the median the best measure of center to summarize the weight of cats in this data set? Why or why not?

On Your Own

4. Write two statistical questions that could be answered using the dot plot in Question 3. Answer your questions. Remember, a statistical question gives us information about a set of data, not an individual piece of data.

5. Describe each data distribution. Which of the following are symmetric?

a)

1 2 3 4 5 6 7

b)

1 2 3 4 5 6

c)

1 2 3 4 5 6

6. Make up a data set that satisfies the following conditions. Your data set must have a minimum of seven values in it.

   a) It has a mode of 3 and a median of 5.

   b) It has a mode of 3 and a median of 3.

   c) It has a mode of 5 and a median of 3.

   d) It has a range of 10 and a median of 3.

7. Ms. Salinas is examining the scores on a pre-test she gave her math students. She plans to use these data to improve her instruction; she will spend more time teaching topics that students know little about and less time on topics that students already understand. The data set below shows the students' scores out of 25 possible points.

   6 11 7 25 3 8 7 7 10 4 8 6

   a) Determine the two measures of center for this set of data. Also give the mode.

   b) One score does not seem to fit in this data set. What is this score? What does it tell Ms. Salinas?

   c) Remove this one extreme score and recalculate the mean and the median.

   d) Which measure of center is most affected by a data value that is very different from the rest of the set? Explain.

8. Find the mean of each data set.

a) 0, 0, 0, 40, 0

b) 8, 8, 8, 8, 8

c) 10, 11, 6, 8, 5

d) Compare the range of the three data sets in Parts a–c.

e) Why is it important to examine the distribution and the mean together when describing a data set?

9. a) On graph paper, plot four points that form the vertices of a rectangle. Make sure each vertex is in a different quadrant. List the coordinates of the four vertices.

b) Find the lengths of the four sides of the rectangle.

10. What is the difference between an expression and an equation? Write a definition for each term and give two examples of each.

11. St. Bernard puppies grow to be enormous! They are supposed to gain weight at a rate of 3 pounds per week. Tiger, the puppy, weighs 40 pounds at 3 months. Based on this growth rate, how many pounds will he weigh when he is 1 year old?

12. Determine the values of a, b, c and d in these multiplication puzzles.

a)

×	10	c
a	300	d
b	50	20

b)

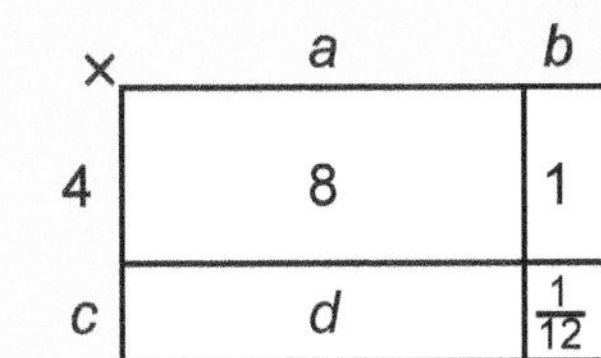

13. Rewrite these fractions and decimals as percents.

a) $\frac{5}{8}$

b) 0.02

c) 0.8

d) $\frac{2}{5}$

e) $\frac{1}{3}$

Box-and-Whisker Plots

Start It Off

Statistical questions are different from everyday questions you might ask. The answers to statistical questions give us information about a set of data where the data values vary. For example, "How old are you?" is *not* a statistical question. It gives us information about only one data value and you wouldn't expect various answers. But "How old are the students in my school?" is a statistical question because we will learn about a set of data that most likely has variation in its values.

1. Talk with a partner and decide which of the following are statistical questions.
   a) How many siblings do sixth graders in my class have?
   b) What size sneaker does my best friend wear?
   c) Am I going to have homework this evening?
   d) What is the capitol of the United States?
   e) How long in centimeters are students' feet at the start of sixth grade?
   f) How many days are in the month of February?
   g) How many days does it snow in Maine in the month of February?
   h) What is the length of time students have for recess in school?
2. Write a statistical question you would like to investigate.

The Median and Interquartile Range

The median is a measure of center that tells us about the middle of a data set. In Lesson 3.1 you answered the statistical question: "What is the average height of a student in our classroom?" The median gave you one height that could be used to summarize the height of everyone. But does that mean everyone is that height? It is important to know about the spread of the data in a set or how much variation is in the data set in order to answer questions. In this lesson you will investigate this further.

MATHEMATICALLY SPEAKING

▶ box-and-whisker plot (box plot)

A graph that can be used to give us information about the variability of a data set is a box-and-whisker plot, often referred to as a box plot. A box plot lets us see both the spread and shape of the data and some measures of center.

For the International Festival, one student from Cooke City, Montana, was looking up information on the internet about his ancestors, Native Americans who were part of the Crow Tribe. He came across some information about the weather in this part of the country. Do you live in a part of the country where it snows? Montana is an especially snowy state and Cooke City gets a huge amount of snow! The yearly snowfall amounts in inches in Cooke City, Montana, from 2001–2011 are listed below. These values have been rounded to the nearest inch.

248 254 175 198 242 200 260 278 137 257 179

1. What is the median and range?
2. Describe the distribution of data.
3. Use the box plot below of annual snowfall amounts to draw some conclusions.

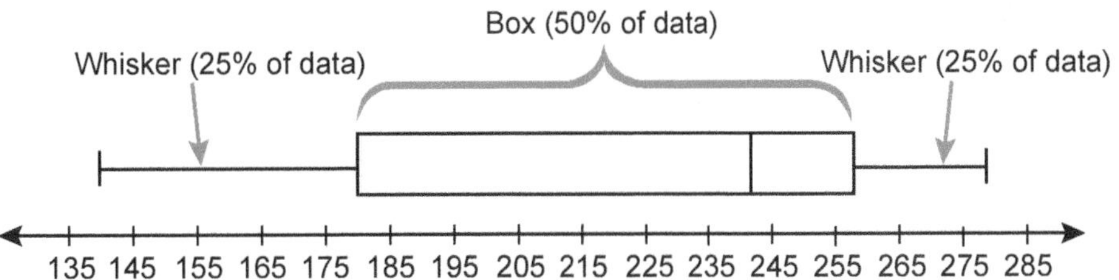

   a) How does a box plot show the greatest and least values in a data set?
   b) What percent of the data from the set are somewhere along the whiskers?
   c) What percent of the data from the set are represented by the "box?"
   d) Look at the data values. What does the line segment inside the box represent?

It looks like the data set has been divided into 4 equal parts.

Two sixth graders, Elsie and Anthony, were talking about the box plot.

Yeah. 25% is one whisker, 50% is in the box and 25% is along the other whisker.

4. a) Do you agree or disagree with the students? Explain.

b) The median is not in the center of the box. What does that tell you about the spread of the data? Think about how many values have to be to the right and to the left of the median.

Example

To make a box plot, follow the directions below.

- Put the data in order and identify the minimum median, and maximum values.

137 175 179 198 200 **242** 248 254 257 260 278

minimum median maximum

- Notice that the median divides the data set in half. Examine the half of the data that comes before the median. There are 5 numbers. The median of this lower half of the set is called the first quartile (Q1). Find the first quartile and circle the number (179). (When there is an even number of data values, average the two middle values.)
- Look at the 5 numbers that come after the median of the data set. Find the median of this upper portion of the data. It is called the third quartile (Q3). Circle this number (257). (When there is an even number of data values, average the two middle values.)
- The interquartile range (IQR) is another way to measure the spread of the data in a set. It is the range of the middle 50% of the data and is found by subtracting the first quartile from the third quartile ($Q3 - Q1 = IQR$; $257 - 179 = 78$). Statisticians often use the IQR because it is not affected by the minimum or maximum data points.
- To create a box plot, start with the five-number summary. The five-number summary consists of the following 5 numbers: the minimum, Q1, median, Q3 and maximum. Mark these five numbers above a number line. Be sure to use equal intervals on the number line.
- Draw a box that contains all the data points between the first and the third quartiles. Draw a whisker from the first quartile to the minimum value and a whisker from the third quartile to the maximum value. Finally, draw a line segment in the box to represent the median.

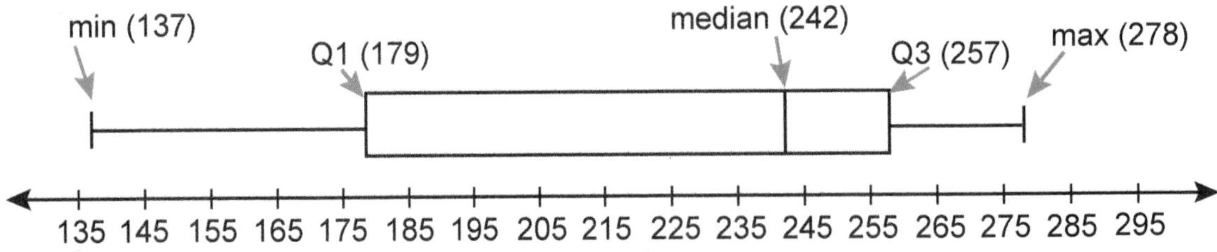

MATHEMATICALLY SPEAKING

- first quartile (Q1)
- third quartile (Q3)
- interquartile range (IQR)
- five-number summary

5. Based on these data, how much snowfall should someone expect if they were moving to Cooke City? Write three sentences.

6. Sometimes it is better to have more data points in order to identify trends. What if we examine 20 years of snowfall amounts in Cooke City? Here are the annual amounts of snowfall in inches from 1992 through 2000. Combine these with the other snowfall amounts from 2001–2011 and determine the five-number summary.

176	140	142	211	194	156	237	220	192

7. Draw a box plot that includes all 20 pieces of data on annual snowfall in inches in Cooke City, MT.

8. Use the box plots from Question 7 and the Example to answer these questions.

   a) Compare the interquartile ranges (IQRs) for the two Cooke City box plots. What do you notice?

   b) Why might the IQR be a useful measure for examining the distribution in a data set?

   c) Why did the median annual snowfall change in the two box plots?

   d) Using the larger data set, describe the annual snowfall in this part of Montana.

9. Examine the following three box plots that show the yearly amount of snowfall in inches in Fargo, ND, Westchester County, NY, and Blacksburg, VA, over many years.

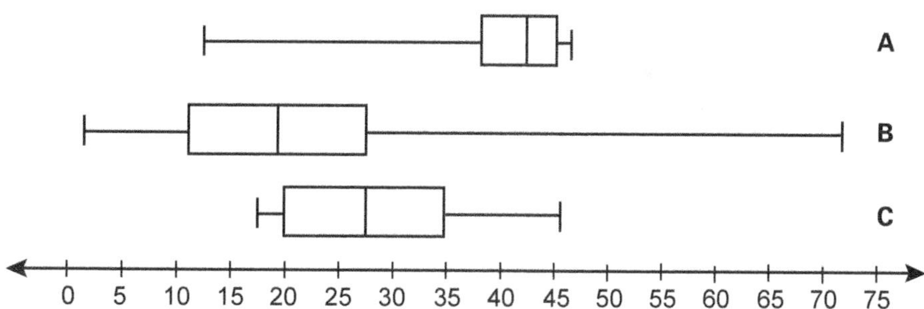

   a) Match each box plot with one of the three places. Think about the amounts of snow the three locations may receive or gather some information on the internet about the weather in these places.

   b) The box in box plot A is very short. What does this tell you about the annual amount of snow in that city?

   c) Is it possible to tell from a box plot how many years of data were collected? Why or why not?

   d) The boxes in B and C are about the same size. But the full box plots are very different. Describe the spread of data for both.

Wrap It Up

Describe the key features of a box plot. What types of information can you get from the interquartile range?

MATHEMATICALLY SPEAKING

- box-and-whisker plot (box plot)
- five-number summary
- first quartile
- interquartile range (IQR)
- third quartile

LESSON 3.2 SECTION 3

On Your Own

Write About It

1. Explain what the five-number summary tells us about a data set. Use the data from Question 7 in the lesson to provide examples.

2. How do you find the five-number summary when there are an even number of data values in a set?

3. The data below are the minimum monthly temperatures in Anchorage, Alaska.

   8 11 17 29 39 48 53 50 42 28 15 12

   a) Identify the median and range.

   b) Give the Q1, Q3 and IQR (interquartile range).

   c) What do the range and the IQR tell you about the temperature in Anchorage? Explain.

   d) Based on these data, predict a range for the likely minimum monthly temperatures in Anchorage in future years. Explain your thinking.

4. Hourly wages for summer jobs for students vary. Here are the hourly wages for a sampling of summer workers at the SummerTemp Company.

   $8.00 $8.50 $8.25 $9.00 $11.00
   $8.00 $12.50 $50.00 $8.00 $7.75

   a) Give the five-number summary for this data set. What does it tell you about typical summer hourly wages, based on this sample?

   b) Kendra stated: "I'm applying to the SummerTemp Company for a job. They advertise that the mean summer hourly salary is $13.10." What would you say to Kendra about her chances of earning $13.10 an hour at SummerTemp, based on the data?

On Your Own

5. a) Create a box plot for the data in Question 4.

   b) What does the size of the interquartile range tell you about a data set?

6. Ms. Elmore teaches two different sixth-grade math classes, Class A and Class B. She gave both classes a test on statistics and then made box plots showing the results.

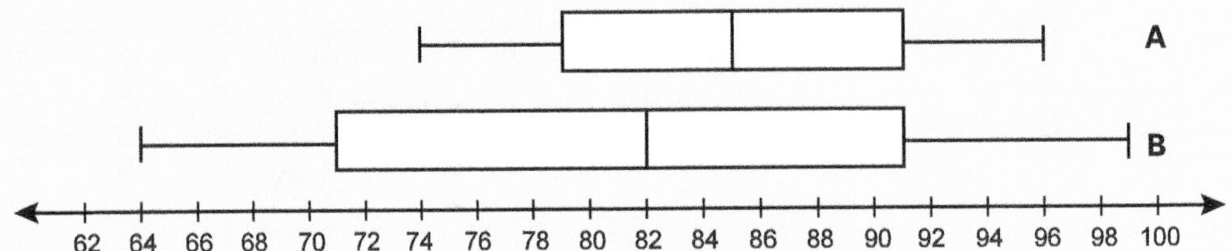

   a) Give the five-number summary for both classes.

   b) What is the range and the IQR for each class?

   c) What might have caused the difference in test results between the classes?

   d) Which class was better prepared to take the test? How can you tell?

7. Use the data in Question 6 above. Compare the medians and the IQRs. Why is it important to always consider measures of center AND measures of variation?

8. The ratio of the white keys to black keys on a piano is 13 : 9. If there are 36 black keys on a specific keyboard, what is the total number of black and white keys on it?

9. Estimate each difference by rounding to the nearest integer and subtracting. Then check your conclusion by calculating the actual difference.

   a) $12.3 - 9.786$ **b)** $16\frac{1}{4} - 7\frac{2}{3}$ **c)** $|-4.1| - |0.035|$

10. Imagine the dot pattern below continues by adding the same number of dots to each subsequent term.

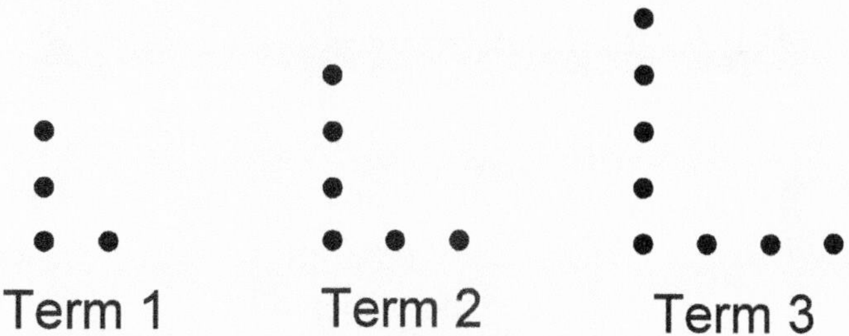

   a) Write the recursive rule for this pattern.

   b) Write the explicit rule for this pattern.

   c) How many dots will be in Term 15?

11. Sean was graphing $x \leq -4$ on a number line. If he graphed the inequality correctly, explain why. If he graphed it incorrectly, re-graph the solution.

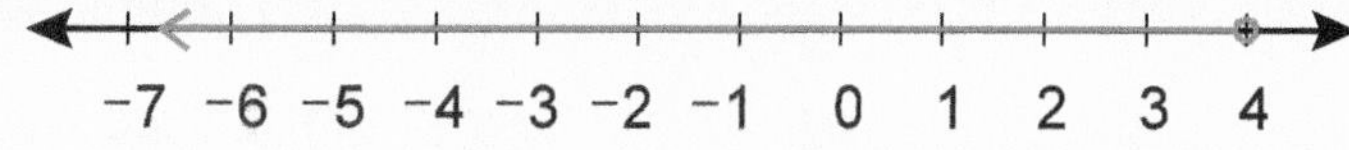

12. Twelve ears of corn cost $8.00. At that price, what is the cost of two ears of corn?

The Mean

Start It Off

1. What measures of center are available for describing a data set?
2. What measures of spread are available for describing a data set?
3. How do you decide which measure of center and which measure of spread should be used when describing a data set?

Equal Sharing

A carnival contacted the Eastside Middle School to find out if they might offer rides and games to students during the International Festival. The school agreed since having rides and games at the festival would attract even more people!

Game and ride tickets were printed up and distributed to students, but a mistake was made. Every student did not receive the same number of tickets. Use either square tiles or square pieces of paper to represent the tickets and to solve the following problems. Do not compute to find the mean.

1. Work in groups of 4. Distribute 13 tickets to one person, 2 to another person, 10 to the third person, and 7 to the fourth person in your group. Now redistribute the tickets so that everyone has the same number of tickets. What is the mean number?
2. a) If your group had started with 4 fewer tickets, how would that have affected the mean? What is the new mean?

   b) If your group had started with 10 additional tickets, how would that have affected the mean? Explain.
3. Two new students join your group. Assuming you have the same total number of tickets as in Question 1, what is going to happen to the mean now? Explain.
4. Imagine that one student in your group of 4 has 51 tickets, while the others have 2, 3 and 4 tickets.

   a) What is the effect of this large number on the mean?

   b) What are the features of data sets where the mean gives a good summary of the data?

5. In another group of 4 students, 3 students have 7, 12 and 20 tickets. How many tickets must the fourth person in the group have if the group wants a mean of 18 tickets? Explain your reasoning.

A Balancing Point

You can think of the mean as the balancing point in a set of data. Values on either side of the mean can be compared so that sets of two or more numbers are an equal distance from the mean. Examine the number line below that is being used as a balance scale. The number 6 is the mean and the "balance point."

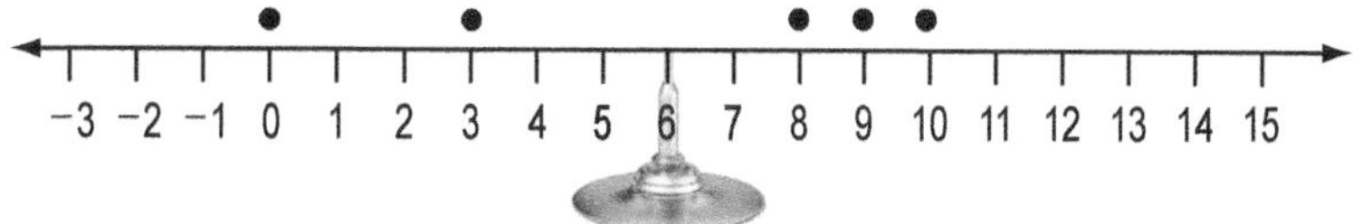

6. **a)** Identify two numbers that are the same distance from the mean (one below and one above).

   b) Explain how the remaining two numbers above the mean balance the one number below the mean.

   c) Identify two new numbers that when placed on the balance scale keeps the mean at 6.

Linda had an interesting way of thinking about the mean. She made bars to represent the number of tickets 5 students had and drew a line at 7 to represent the mean.

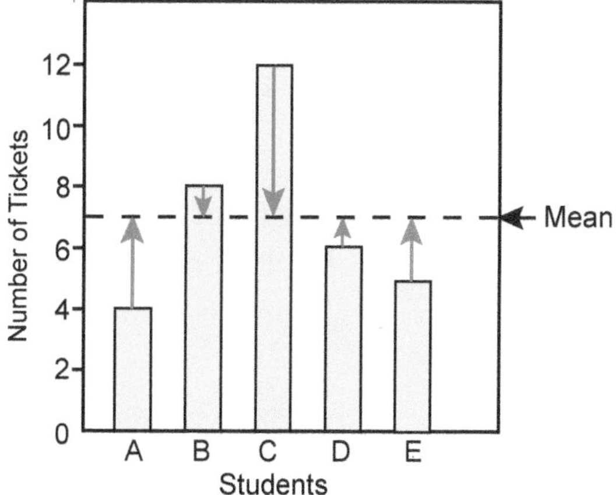

7. **a)** Discuss with a partner how Linda's drawing shows that the data values balance around the mean.

   b) Find the distance from the mean of each number below the mean. Then find the sum of the distances.

c) Compare your answer to Part b with the sum of the distances from the mean of the numbers above the mean.

8. Leonard has taken 5 math quizzes and has 1 more quiz this term. His scores were 72%, 80%, 85%, 92% and 100%. He wants his mean quiz score to be 88%, which will be a B+. Use a bar graph and the idea of the mean as a balance point to help Leonard figure out what score he needs on his last quiz in order to have a mean score of 88%.

Mean Absolute Deviation

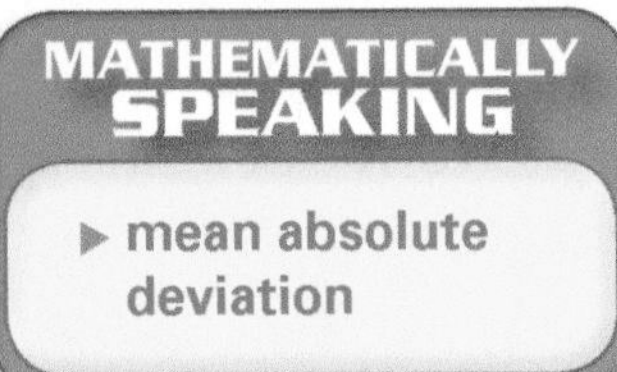

When describing data sets, it is important to also consider the spread of the data. So far you have described spread using the range and the interquartile range (IQR) of a data set. Another value that describes the spread of data is called the mean absolute deviation. The mean absolute deviation helps you make decisions about data sets that have the same mean but different amounts of spread. The deviation from the mean is the difference of a data value from the mean value of the data set.

To find the mean absolute deviation, you must determine the average distance each data point is from the mean.

- If a data set has a smaller mean absolute deviation, the data points are not spread very far on either side of the mean. The average of the distances from the mean is small. There is not a lot of variability in the data set.

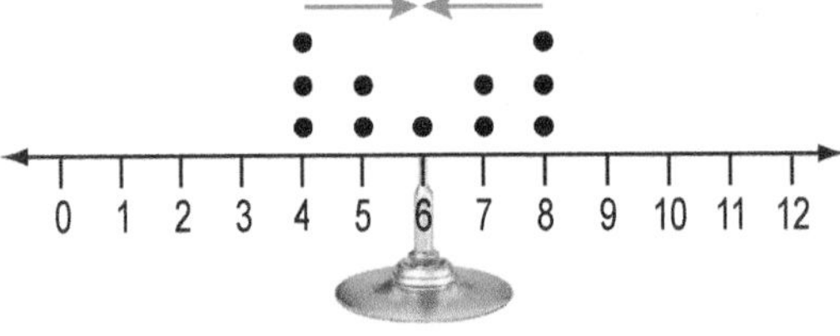

- If a data set has a larger mean absolute deviation, the data points are spread out more and are farther from the mean. The average of the distances from the mean is large. There is more variability in the data set.

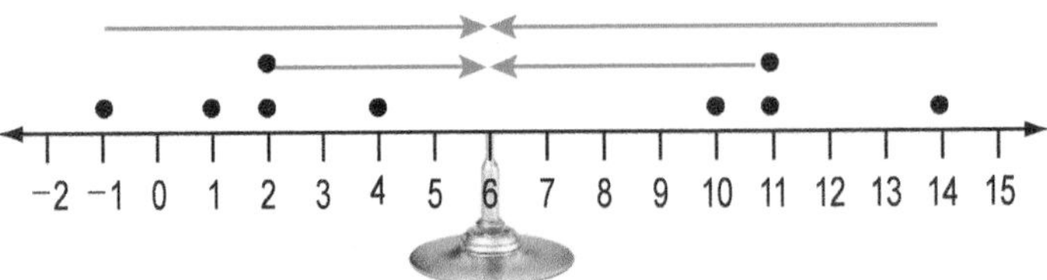

9. At the International Festival, students competed in a beanbag toss game. The scores of two students are below.

Phillipe:	6	7	8	10	4	7
Monique:	1	10	12	2	14	3

a) How many turns did each of the students have?

b) What is the mean number of points that each student scored in the game?

c) What is the range of points scored by each student in the game?

d) Copy the table below. Fill in the scores for Phillipe in the first column. In the second column, record the difference from the mean for each score. If the score is less than the mean, record the distance as a negative number. If the score is greater than the mean, record the distance as a positive number. In column 3, record the absolute value of the numbers in column 2.

Data Value	Difference from Mean (Deviation)	Absolute Value
6	$^{-}1$	1

e) Calculate the sum of the third column.

f) Divide the sum from Part e by the number of data values in order to find the mean absolute deviation for Phillipe's scores.

g) Follow the same procedure to determine the mean absolute deviation for Monique's scores.

10. How does the mean absolute deviation help you compare and describe the differences between Phillipe's and Monique's scores?

11. Did you notice that the absolute value was used to calculate the mean deviation in Question 9? What would happen if you did not use the absolute values of the differences from the mean? Use your data to demonstrate what would happen.

Wrap It Up

You can find the mean of a set of data using the equal-sharing idea or the balance idea. Explain both and what the mean tells us about a data set. Why do we need to also include information about the variability of the set, such as the mean absolute deviation?

MATHEMATICALLY SPEAKING

- mean absolute deviation

LESSON 3.3 SECTION 3

On Your Own

Write About It

1. You have learned that the mean is a number that is used to summarize the data values in a set. Explain to a student who was absent what this mean number represents.

Hint
See page 150

2. Find the mean of each of the following data sets by redistributing to create equal shares.

   a) {6, 10, 11, 13}
   b) {17, 5, 20, 14, 9}
   c) {8, 8, 8, 3, 8, 19}
   d) {1, 6, 1, 6}

3. Explain your strategy for solving Question 2d.

4. Make up a situation where you think the mean would be a good measure of center for the data set. Give data values and find the mean.

5. Examine the three box plots below that show the ages of students in three different schools.

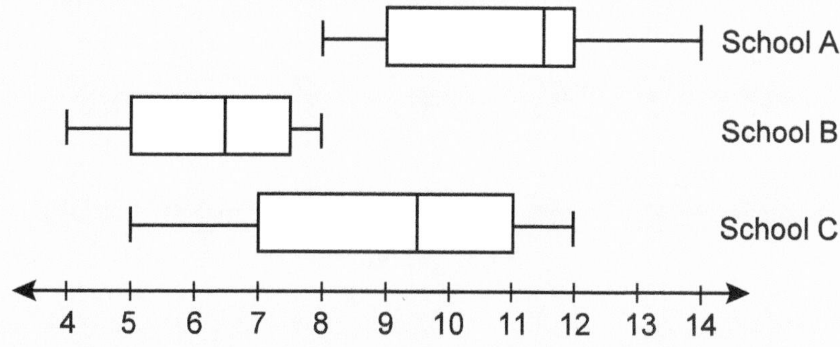

   a) Which school is a grades K–1 school? How do you know?
   b) What does the box plot for School A tell you about 12-year-old students at that school?
   c) What statements can you make about the students at School C?

6. Make up data sets with the following characteristics.

   a) Mean of 10; 8 data values
   b) Mean of 10; spread of 2
   c) Mean of 10; spread of 30

On Your Own

7. The drinks committee at the International Festival wants to advertise that the mean price of six different drinks is $1.25. They are selling five different drinks at the following prices: $1.00, $1.25, $2.00, $1.50 and $0.50. How much should they sell the sixth drink for in order to be able to say that the mean cost of a drink at their stand is $1.25? Explain.

8. Coach Addition wants to compare the points scored by her players during two different basketball games.

Game 1:	6	2	8	3	12	4	5	10
Game 2:	4	6	8	14	8	2	0	5

   a) How many players are on the team?

   b) What is the mean number of points for the players for each game?

   c) What is the range in points scored for each game?

   d) Calculate the mean absolute deviation for each game.

   e) Do you think the scoring in the two games is equivalent?

9. Create two box plots to compare the scores in Games 1 and 2 from Question 8.

10. Without calculating, which one of the two sets below has the smaller mean absolute deviation? Why?

Set 1:	10	11	12	13	14	15	16	17	18	19	20
Set 2:	12	12	13	13	14	14	14	15	15		

11. When buying a car, people are interested in learning how many miles per gallon (MPG) the car gets for highway and city driving. Below are the MPG data values for city driving for 20 SUVs.

    10, 11, 12, 12, 13, 14, 15, 16, 17, 18, 19, 20, 20, 21, 22, 24, 28, 30, 32, 34

    Find the mean MPG for city driving. Do you think the mean is the best measure of center for this data set?

12. **a)** Do you think the mean absolute deviation for the data set in Question 11 will be high or low?

b) Calculate the mean absolute deviation.

c) Write a few sentences about the MPG that SUVs typically get for city driving. Use your two numbers (mean and mean absolute deviation) and explain what these numbers mean in terms of MPG.

13. Determine the median, Q1 and Q3 for the data set in Question 11.

14. Draw a box plot to display the data from Question 11.

15. What are some explanations for why there is such variability in this data set?

16. **a)** Paige's family is putting new carpet in her bedroom. Her room is square and measures 11 feet by 11 feet. If carpeting costs $2.15 per square foot, what is the total cost of the carpet?

b) Installation costs are 10% of the cost of the carpet. What is the total cost of carpeting Paige's bedroom?

17. Write these fractions as decimals and percents.

a) $\frac{3}{4}$

b) $\frac{7}{8}$

c) $\frac{1}{3}$

d) $\frac{3}{5}$

e) $\frac{7}{10}$

18. Solve each inequality below and graph it on a number line.

a) $5 + x > 12$ **b)** $\frac{2}{3}x \leq 1$ **c)** $3m \geq 2\frac{1}{4}$

19. The volume of a rectangular prism is 24 cubic centimeters. Give four different possibilities for the dimensions of the prism.

20. Simplify each expression.

a) $5^2 - 2(7-1)$

b) $3.2 - \frac{1}{2} + \frac{2}{5}$

c) 5% of 180

d) 92 − 13.678

LESSON 3.4 Statistical Displays

Sixth graders decided to survey students in the school in order to choose the music for the International Festival. Answer the following questions using the bar graph below.

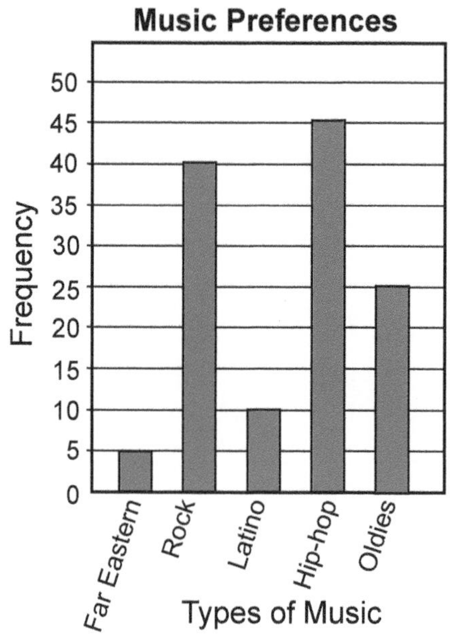

1. How many students chose "oldies" as their favorite type of music?
2. Compare the number of students who like Latino music to those who prefer rock music.
3. **a)** What type of data are being represented?

   b) Is there a mean or median value for this data? Why or why not?
4. The frequency, or number of pieces of data represented by each bar, is shown on the vertical axis. Use this information to determine the total number of students surveyed about their music preference.
5. Write a statistical question that might be answered by using data from the bar graph.

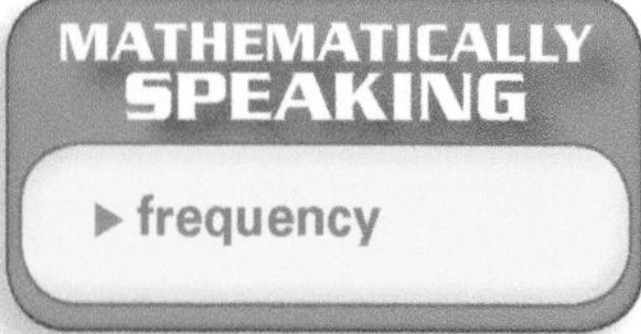

There are a variety of ways that data are represented using graphs. Dot plots, bar graphs, box plots, pictographs and circle graphs are all used. In this lesson, you will learn about two new types of data displays: histograms and stem-and-leaf plots. Histograms tend to be used with very large data sets, while stem-and-leaf plots are more practical for smaller, numerical sets.

Histograms

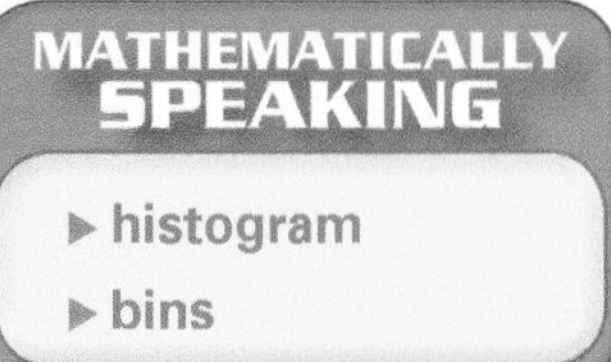

Remember when you examined the annual amount of snowfall in Cooke City, Montana, in Lesson 3.2? Examine how these data from 2001 through 2011 are shown in a histogram. A histogram is similar to a bar graph but each bar represents the number of times a piece of data occurs within a specific interval. This is the frequency of data in that interval. The intervals in a histogram all have the same width, and the bars touch each other.

The intervals along the x-axis are called bins. All of the bins in a histogram must be the same width. A bin includes the value on the left of the bar but doesn't include the value on the right of the bar.

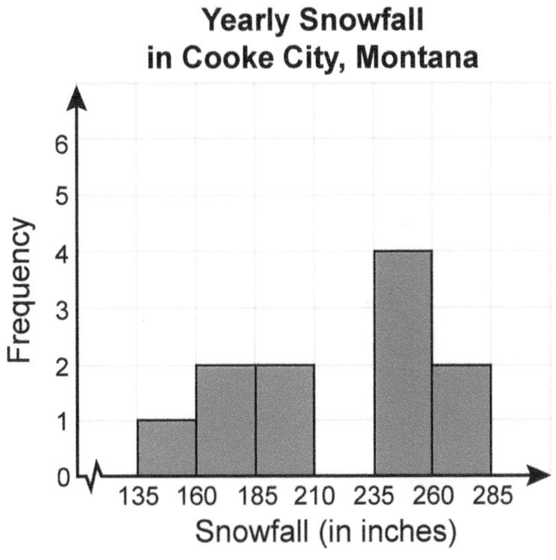

Data source: Western Regional Climate Center, http://www.wrcc.dri.edu/cgi-bin/cliMONtsnf.pl?mt1995

1. List three things about a histogram that are the same as a bar graph.
2. Use the histogram above to answer the following questions.
   a) What is the size of each interval or bin?
   b) Between which two snowfall amounts was the frequency the least? Write these amounts in terms of feet and inches.
   c) How many years are represented on this histogram? How do you know?
   d) In which interval did snowfall occur most often? How can you tell?
   e) Can you determine the mode of this data set? Why or why not?
   f) Describe the data using the following terms: gaps, clusters and range.

3. **a)** Create a question that could be answered using the data from the histogram.

b) Create a question about snowfall in Cooke City that cannot be answered based on the data in the histogram.

Whereas some places in the United States are cold and snowy, other locations can be very, very hot. Phoenix, Arizona, experienced a very hot July in 2012. Examine the table of the maximum temperatures recorded.

Date	Max Temp °F	Date	Max Temp °F	Date	Max Temp °F	Date	Max Temp °F
1	109	9	113	17	103	25	106
2	106	10	112	18	106	26	107
3	100	11	111	19	107	27	109
4	91	12	105	20	109	28	101
5	99	13	95	21	108	29	104
6	104	14	97	22	105	30	100
7	109	15	100	23	106	31	104
8	110	16	103	24	104		

Data source: Western Regional Climate Center, http://nowdata.rcc-acis.org/PSR/pubACIS_results

Nancy organized these data in a list from least to greatest.

91 95 97 99 100 100 100 101 103 103 104
104 104 104 105 105 106 106 106 106 107 107
108 109 109 109 109 110 111 112 113

4) **a)** What was the median maximum temperature in Phoenix in July 2012?

b) What is the mode of this data set? What do the mode and median tell us about this data set?

c) What was the range of maximum temperatures in July 2012?

5. Examine the histogram of these data.

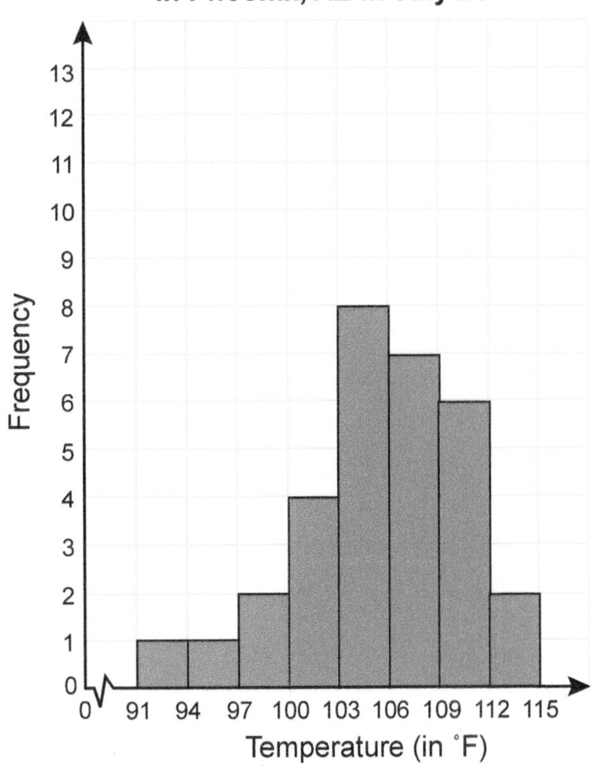

a) Discuss with your partner what you think the √‾ symbol along the x-axis represents.

b) Can you determine the mode and median for this data set by just using the histogram? Why or why not?

c) What temperatures are included in the first bin of the histogram?

d) What size are the bins in this histogram?

6. a) How many days was the temperature at least 100°F but less than 103°F?

b) How many days was the temperature at least 106°F?

c) How many days was the temperature less than 100°F?

d) If there was one more bin to the far right on the histogram above, what temperatures would it include?

Stem-and-Leaf Plots

Histograms are used to show trends in large data sets. But did you notice that you cannot tell what the individual data values are in a histogram? Sometimes it is important to be able to see the actual data values. In that case, a better data display is the stem-and-leaf plot. Stem-and-leaf plots are created using the numerical values in a data set. They are similar to a bar graph , except stem-and-leaf plots display numerical data and bar graphs display categorical data.

Are you a basketball fan? What are the most points ever scored by a player in an individual game in the NBA? Amazingly, Wilt Chamberlain scored 100 points in 1962, followed by 81 points by Kobe Bryant in 2006! Then there are a lot of players that have scored 60 or 70 points. The top 20 scores are shown in the stem-and-leaf plot below. The "stem" is to the left of the line and represents a specific place value, such as tens. The "leaves" are the remaining place values, arranged from least to greatest.

Stem	Leaves
6	5 5 6 7 7 7 7 8 8 9
7	0 1 1 2 3 3 3 8
8	1
9	
10	0

Key: 7 | 2 means 72

In a stem-and-leaf plot, you can see the actual data values. Notice there are two times when a player has scored 71 points in a game, shown by the stem of 7, representing 70, and the two 1's to the right. A stem-and-leaf plot always has a key, which tells everyone how to interpret the numbers.

7. a) Why can you find the mode of the data set from a stem-and-leaf plot? What is the mode of this set?

b) Determine the median of the data set. How did you do it?

c) There is nothing to the right of the stem of 9. What does this mean?

8. In the 2012 Olympics, the U.S. women's basketball team beat France for the gold medal. Below are the number of points scored in that game by each of the 12 players on each team.

USA:	3	8	11	6	7	4	4	3	9	6	4	21
FRANCE:	8	2	0	12	12	8	0	4	0	0	4	0

Data source: Official site of the London 2012 Olympic and Paralympic Games, http://www.london2012.com/basketball/event/women/match=bkw400101/index.html

a) Create two back-to-back stem-and-leaf plots of these data. Namely, put the stem in the middle, as shown below, to represent tens (0, 10, 20 and 30). Put the USA leaves on one side and the French leaves on the other. Be sure to include a key so that everyone knows which place value the stem represents.

French leaves	Stem	USA leaves
	0	
	1	
	2	
	3	

b) Describe each data set using your stem-and-leaf plots. Remember to use measures of center and to address the distribution of the data.

c) Compare the two stem-and-leaf plots. What was the final score of the game?

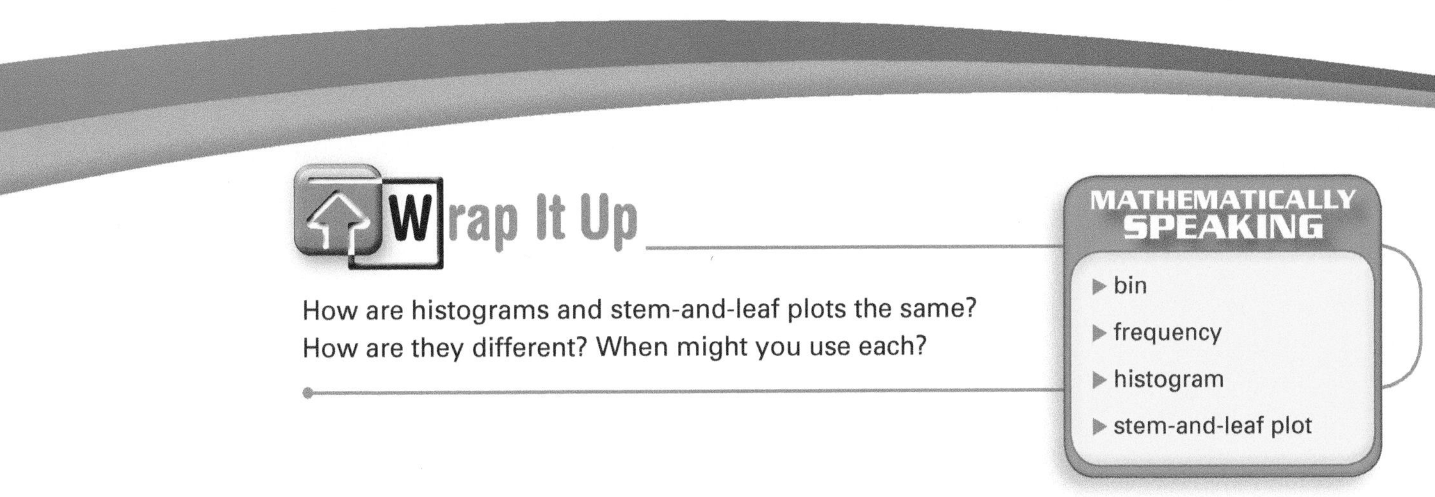

How are histograms and stem-and-leaf plots the same? How are they different? When might you use each?

On Your Own

1. Which measures of center can you determine using a stem-and-leaf plot? Using a histogram? Can you describe the variation in a data set using either graph? Explain.

2. Students in Ms. Zito's sixth-grade class kept track of how many minutes they spent on their math homework one evening. Use the histogram to answer the following questions.

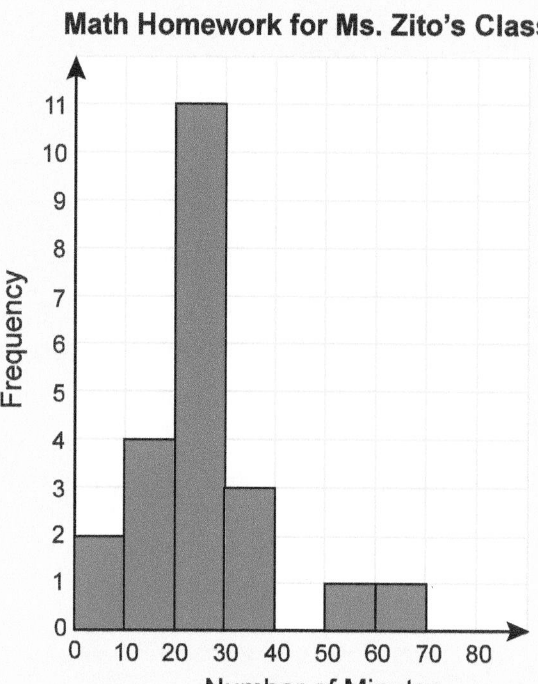

   a) How many students are in Ms. Zito's class?

   b) How many students spent at least 20 minutes but less than 30 minutes on homework?

   c) Is it possible to determine the maximum number of minutes a student spent on homework? Why or why not?

   d) Describe in words how much time the second bin represents. How many students spent this amount of time on their math homework?

3. Mr. Grant teaches a different group of sixth grade students. They also kept track of how many minutes they spent on their math homework.

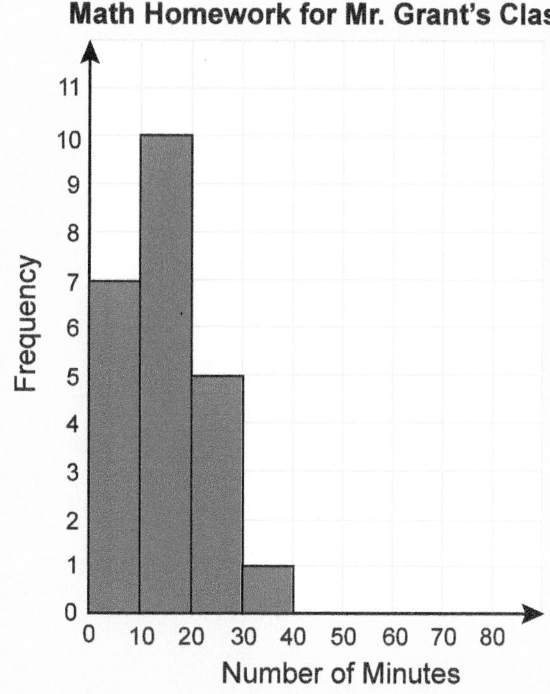

a) Which class was given more math homework: Mr. Grant's class or Ms. Zito's class in Question 2? Explain your reasoning.

b) How many students in Mr. Grant's class spent at least 40 minutes on math homework?

c) What other differences are there between the two classes?

4. The scores on a recent "pop" quiz were: 1, 5, 13, 17, 18, 16, 16, 4, 13, 20, 18, 17, 16, 15, 16. Create a histogram with this data. Make the bins 4 points wide (0–4, 4–8, 8–12, 12–16, 16–20, 20–24).

5. The heights of sixth graders in inches in one class at the Ryan Middle School are listed below.

60 64 63 67 68 58 54 61 62 66 50 53 56 59 54 50 63 49 52

a) Make a histogram using these data.

b) Write three questions that can be answered using the histogram.

6. a) Make a stem-and-leaf plot of the data in Question 5.

b) Give the mean, median, mode and range of the data set.

c) Which display (stem-and-leaf or histogram) gives you a better sense of how these values are distributed? Explain.

On Your Own

7. The following stem-and-leaf plot shows the cost of individual apples for sale at a farmers market.

Stem	Leaf
0	9
1	5 6 6 8
2	1 1 2 4 5 7 7 9
3	3 3 4 5 5 5 6 7 8 8
4	0 1 1 4
5	6

Key: 2 | 5 means 25¢

a) What does 0 | 9 represent? What does 4 | 0 represent?

b) Describe the measures of center and the distribution of the data set.

c) Why might the cost of individual apples differ?

8. Use the distributive property to find the product of $8\frac{1}{3}$ and $3\frac{3}{4}$.

9. At a meeting, 17 people spoke Spanish, 20 spoke English and 9 people spoke both languages. How many people were at the meeting?

10. Find the volume of the following rectangular prism.

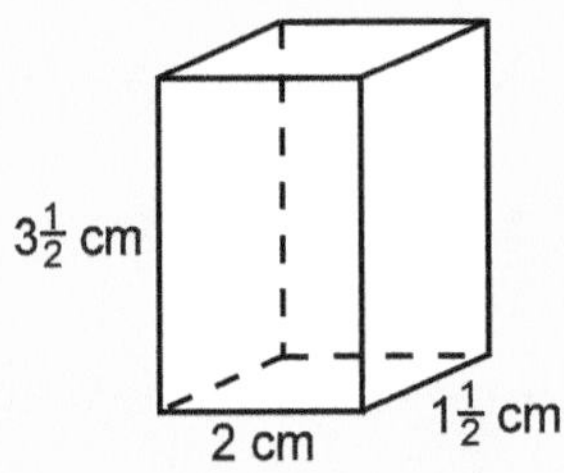

11. **a)** Draw a net of the prism in Question 10.

    b) What is the surface area of the prism?

12. Catherine, Elizabeth and Suzanne decided to go to the movies. Tickets are \$9 each, popcorn is \$5.25 a bucket, and drinks are \$4.85 each. Write an equation to show the total cost for the three of them if everyone gets popcorn but only Catherine gets a drink. How much change will they receive back from \$60.00?

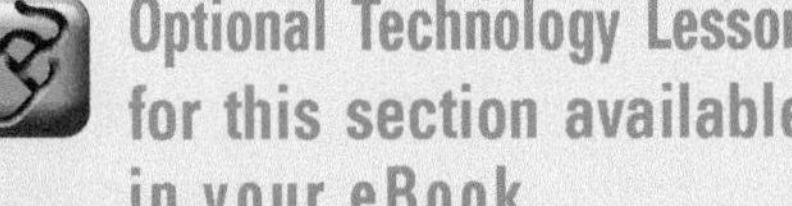

Sum It Up

- Data are facts or numbers that describe something, such as people, places and things. Data are used to answer statistical questions.
- Statistical questions are different from everyday questions. The answers to statistical questions give information about a set of data where the data values vary. "What size sneakers do students in my school wear?" is a statistical question because it is likely there is variation in the responses.
- Data sets can be described using numbers and descriptors. The spread of data, or distribution of data, can be described by noting the range in the data, as well as gaps and clusters. Data can also be described using measures of center.

Measures of Center

- A measure of center is a number that can be used to summarize all of the values in a data set.
- The median is a measure of center. It is the middle value in a data set when the data values are arranged in numerical order.

137 175 179 198 200 **242** 248 254 257 260 278

minimum **median** maximum

- The mean is another measure of center. It is a number that describes the data set as if all values in the data set were the same. It is sometimes called the "arithmetic average." You find the mean by adding all of the data values in a set together and dividing by the number of data items.

$$\text{The mean of } \{4, 8, 2, 10, 16\} \text{ is } \frac{4 + 8 + 2 + 10 + 16}{5} = 8$$

- The mean can also be thought of as a balance point in a set of data.

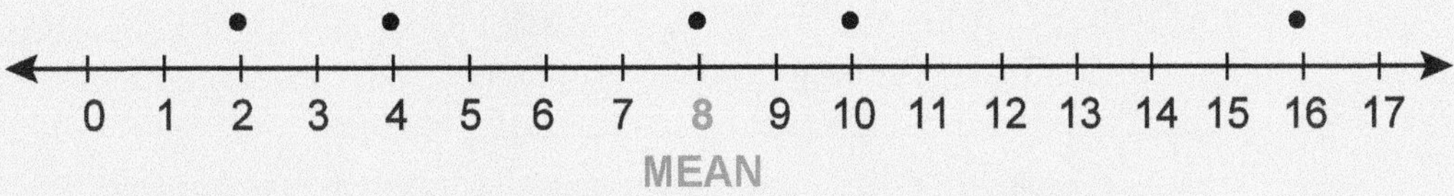

Measures of Variation

- A measure of variation is a number that describes how the data values in a data set vary.
- The range is a measure of variation that describes the spread of a data set. The range is the difference between the maximum value and the minimum value. The range of the data set below is 141, since 278 − 137 = 141.

137 175 179 198 200 **242** 248 254 257 260 278

minimum **median** maximum

- The interquartile range (IQR) is a number that describes the spread of the middle 50% of the data in a data set. It is found by subtracting the first quartile from the third quartile (Q3 − Q1 = IQR). Statisticians often use the IQR because it is not affected by the minimum or maximum data points.

The IQR in the data set below is 78. Q3 − Q1 = IQR 257 − 179 = 78

137 175 **179** 198 200 242 248 254 **257** 260 278

minimum **Q1** median **Q3** maximum

- The mean absolute deviation is another way to describe the spread of data. It is calculated by finding the average distance each data point is from the mean.

If a data set has a smaller mean absolute deviation, the data points are not spread very far on either side of the mean. The average of the distances from the mean is small. There is not a lot of variability in the data set.

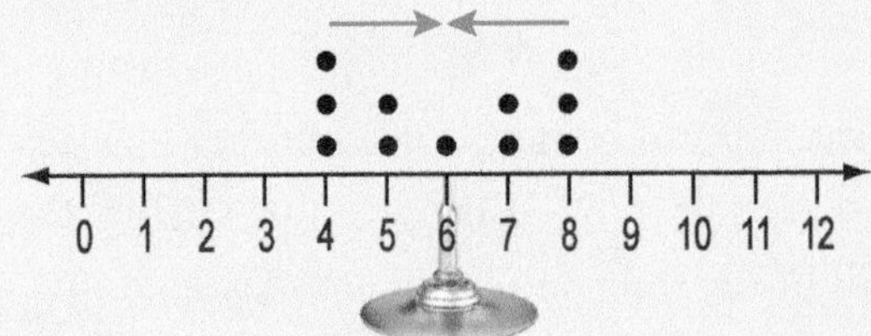

If a data set has a larger mean absolute deviation, the data points are spread out more and are farther from the mean. The average of the distances from the mean is large. There is more variability in the data set.

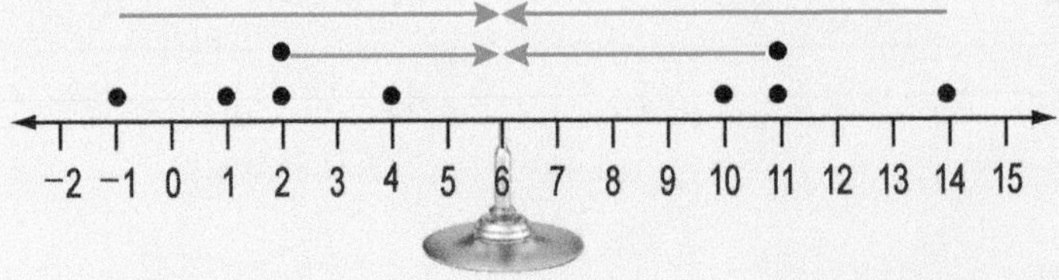

Statistical Displays

There are many different types of statistical displays.

- A dot plot is a graph that shows the frequency of values in a data set along a number line, using a dot (•) to indicate data points. Dot plots (or line plots) are used to graph small sets of data. Gaps and clusters can be seen in a dot plot.

Summer Class Keyboarding Pre-Test

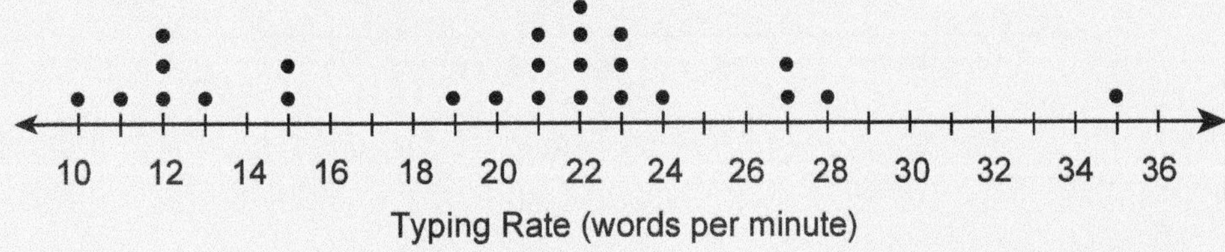

- A stem-and-leaf plot is similar to a bar graph. It shows the values of the numerical data in a set. It is often used to display smaller data sets. The median, range and shape of the data set can be determined using this graph.

Stem	Leaves
6	5 5 6 7 7 7 7 8 8
7	0 1 1 2 3 3 3 8
8	1
9	
10	0

Key: 7| 2 means 72

- A histogram is similar to a bar graph, but each bar represents the number of times a piece of data occurs within a specific interval. The intervals, called bins, all have the same width, and the bars touch each other.

Maximum Daily Temperature in Phoenix, AZ in July 2012

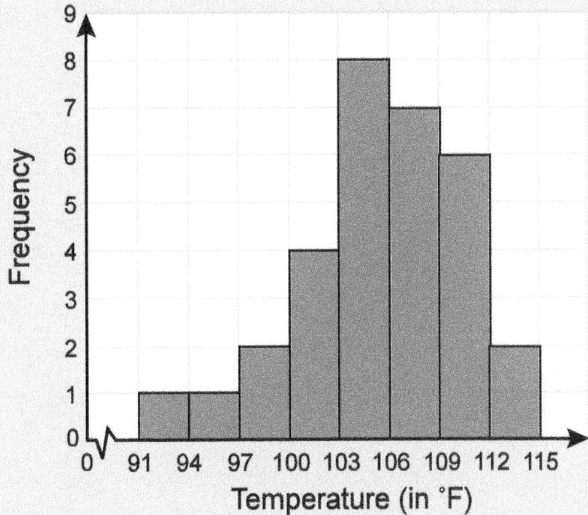

- Histograms are used with large data sets. You cannot determine measures of center by looking at the display, but you can get information about the distribution of the data in the set.
- A box-and-whisker plot (box plot) is a statistical display that lets you see both the spread and shape of the data and some measures of center. However, a box plot does not let you see all of the data values in the set.

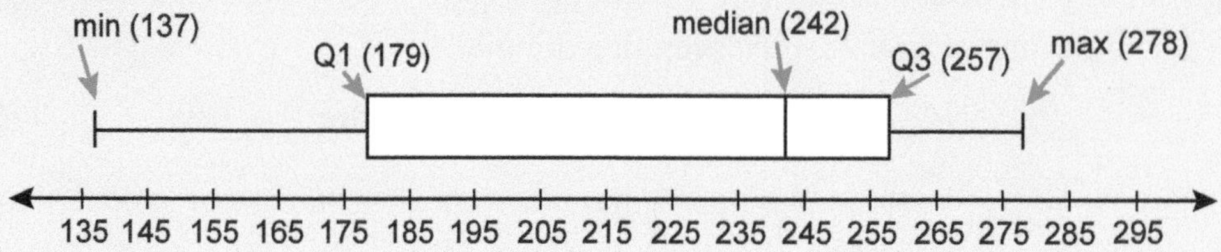

MATHEMATICALLY SPEAKING

Do you know what these mathematical terms mean?

- bimodal
- bin
- box-and-whisker plot (box plot)
- categorical data
- clusters
- data
- deviation from the mean
- distribution of data
- dot plot
- first quartile (Q1)
- five-number summary
- frequency
- gap
- histogram
- interquartile range (IQR)
- mean
- mean absolute deviation
- measure of center
- median
- mode
- numerical data
- range
- stem-and-leaf plot
- third quartile (Q3)

Study Guide

Using Data to Make Comparisons

Part 1. What did you learn?

1. The dot plot below shows the heights of the first 43 U.S. Presidents.

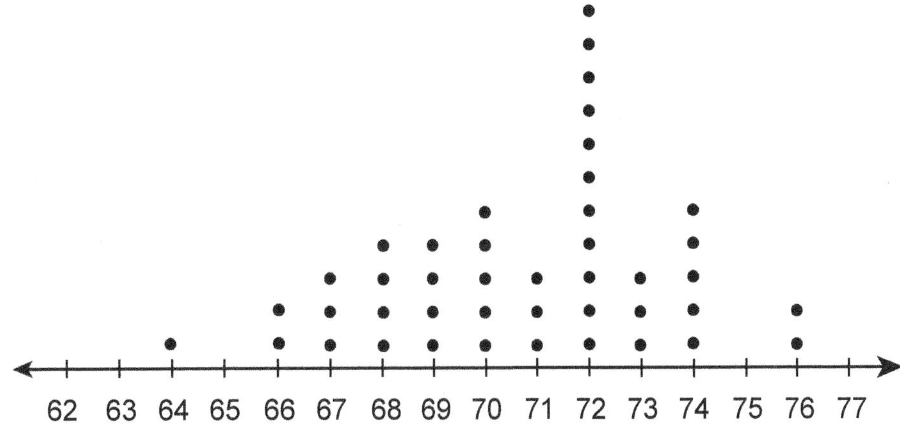

   a. What is the median of the data set?

   b. What is the mode of the data set?

   c. What is the range of the data set?

   d. Describe the distribution of the data set. Be sure to identify any gaps and clusters.

   e. The average height of an American male is approximately 70 inches. Are American presidents typically shorter or taller than the average American male? Explain your thinking.

2. Make a histogram of the data from Question 1. Then, use your histogram to answer the questions below.

   a. What is the bin size of your histogram? How do the labels on the x-axis of your histogram show the bin size?

   b. Compare and contrast the dot plot in Question 1 with your histogram.

3. Mrs. Methany, the school nurse at Hargrove Middle School, is worried about the number of energy drinks the students are drinking. She asked the students in one homeroom to keep track of the number of energy drinks they consumed in one week. Below is a dot plot of the data she collected.

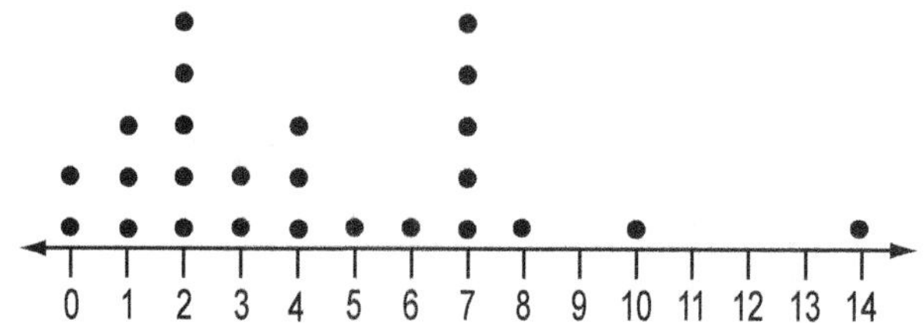

a. Determine a measure of center for this data set. Use this number in a sentence that describes the center in a meaningful way.

b. Based on the measure of center you chose in Part a, determine the variation in the data set. Use this number in a sentence that describes the variation in a meaningful way.

c. Why do you need to know about the center of a data set and the variation in the set in order to answer a statistical question?

4. Students at Williams Middle School have been complaining lately about the length of the line to buy food at lunch. Cheyenne, the student council president,, decided to collect data about the time students spent in line one day in order to address her classmates' concerns. The box plot below displays the data that Cheyenne collected.

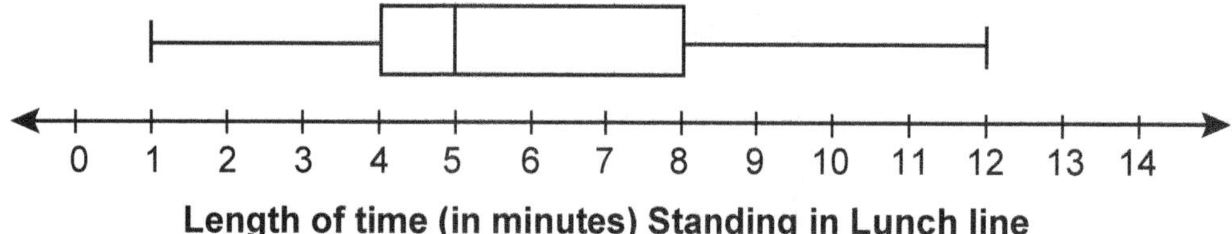

a. Find the five-number summary of the data set.

b. Find the interquartile range.

c. Imagine you are Cheyenne, the student council president. You need to present the findings of your data collection at the next student council meeting. Write a brief speech that summarizes the data in the box plot about wait times in the lunch line.

5. Mr. Sanchez recorded the number of 3-point shots made by each member of his sixth-grade class during one class in September and one class in January. He organized these data in a back-to-back stem-and-leaf plot.

Number of 3-Point Shots Made in September		Number of 3-Point Shots Made in January
9 9 7 7 5 5 0	0	5 7 8 9 9
8 5 5 5 4 4 1	1	0 5
1	2	0 1 2 2 3 6 9 9

Key: 3 | 2 means 32 and 2 | 0 means 20

a. Find the mean of each set of data.

b. Find the range of each set of data.

c. Copy and complete the charts below.

September Data Set		
Data Value	Difference from Mean	Absolute Value

January Data Set		
Data Value	Difference from Mean	Absolute Value

d. Use your work from Part c to find the mean absolute deviation of each data set.

e. Describe at least two other characteristics of the distribution of each data set.

f. Based on your answers to Parts a, b and d, did the average student in this sixth-grade class improve his or her 3-point success rate? Explain your thinking.

6. Tatiana wonders whether people in her town are driving fuel-efficient cars. She asked the owners of a local gas station to record the gas mileage rates of all the cars that came into the gas station one day. The histogram below shows the data that were collected.

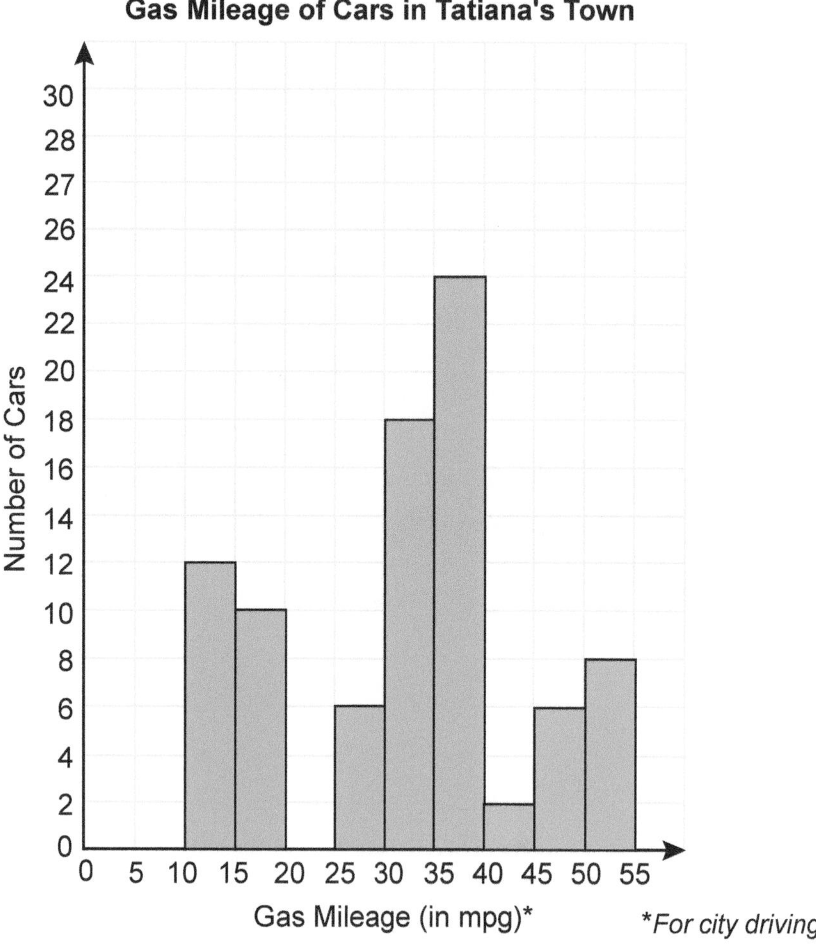

a. What does the term "miles per gallon" mean? What does it mean for a car to be "fuel efficient?"

b. What is the bin size of the histogram?

c. Describe the distribution of the data set.

d. In 2012, a car driven on American roads gets between 20 to 25 miles per gallon, on average. How do the cars in Tatiana's data set compare to this statistic?

e. Tatiana collected this data to see if the people in her town were buying fuel-efficient cars. Based on the data set, how would you answer this question? What other information would you like to know?

7. One value has been erased from each of the line plots below. Use the concept of the mean as a balance point and the dot plot of each data set to find the missing value.

> Example: The line plot should show 4 pieces of data. The mean of the complete data set is 6.
>
> Answer: The missing value is 11. The sum of the distances from the points below the mean to the mean is 5. So the missing data must be 5 units above 6 on the number line.

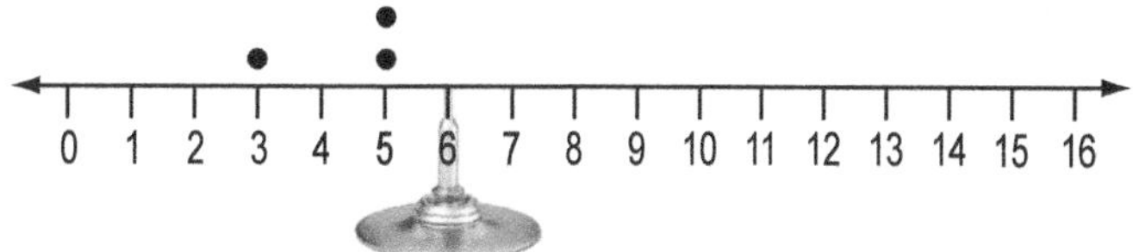

a. The dot plot below should show 5 pieces of data. The mean of the complete data set is 8. What is the value of the missing piece of data?

b. The dot plot below should show 6 pieces of data. The mean of the complete data set is 7. What is the value of the missing piece of data?

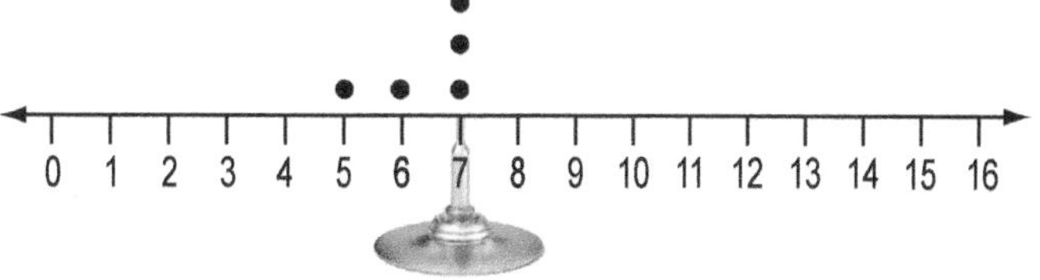

8. The dot plot below should show 6 pieces of data. The mean of the complete data set is 6. Which piece of data should be removed?

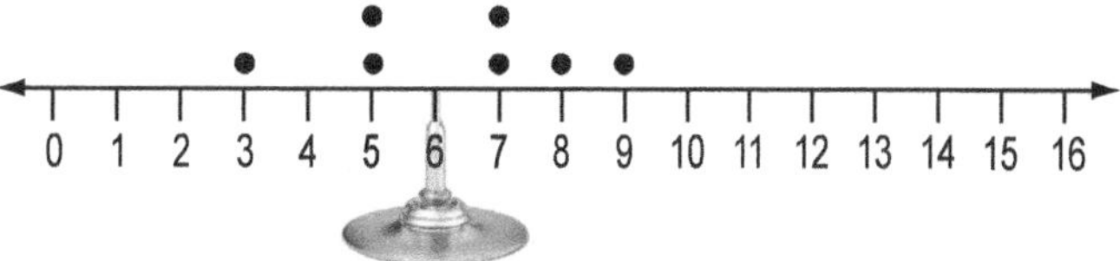

Part 2. What went wrong?

9. Duane's teacher asked him to answer the question below.

Six students borrowed books from the library one day. The chart shows the number of books that each student borrowed.

Ann	Bob	Carlos	Dion	Ellie	Fran
6	5	4	4	6	2

What is the mean of this data set?

Duane added the six numbers and divided the sum by 6. He got 4.5. Duane said, "That can't be right. I learned in class that the mean describes how many books each student borrowed if they all shared the books equally. There's no such thing as 4.5 books!" What is wrong with Duane's reasoning? What could you say or do to help him interpret the mean of 4.5?

10. Ginny was asked to find the median value in the data set below.

Money Spent (per person) on Refreshments at the Movie Theater

$12.50, $0, $10.00, $5.00, $7.50, $0, $10.00

Ginny wrote, "The median value is $5.00." Why might Ginny have chosen $5.00? Why is her answer wrong? What is the median value of the data set?

Unit Study Guide

At This Rate: Focusing on Ratios, Proportions and Statistics

Part 1. What did you learn?

SECTION 1

1. There are many different clubs at the Nielson Middle School. Use the information given to fill in the missing entries in the chart below. Label all the numbers in the ratios you write.

Club	Number of Girls	Number of Boys	Ratio of Girls to Boys Written Using Colon Notation	Ratio of Girls to Boys Written as a Fraction in Simplest Form	Ratio of Boys to Total Number of Students in Simplest Form
Recycling	12	16	a.	b.	c.
Skateboarding	d.	11	e.	f.	$\frac{\text{11 boys}}{\text{20 students}}$
Volunteer	7	g.	7 girls : 21 boys	h.	i.

2. The chart below contains information about the populations and areas of New York and Texas.

State	Population (rounded to the nearest million)	Area (rounded to the nearest thousand square miles)
New York	20,000,000	55,000
Texas	25,000,000	269,000

   a. Use the numbers in the chart to determine which state is more crowded.

   b. Estimate to find the population density of each state.

   c. Do your results from Part b support your answer from Part a? Explain.

3. Janet and Pete compared two different brands of cereal. Each cereal contains raisins and bran flakes. Box A contains more ounces of cereal than Box B. Box B contains about the same number of raisins as Box A. Compare the numbers of raisins per ounce in Box A to Box B.

4. Find x in each of the following proportions.

a. $\frac{5}{12} = \frac{x}{36}$

b. $\frac{21}{x} = \frac{7}{20}$

c. $\frac{x}{7} = \frac{8}{56}$

d. $\frac{4}{9} = \frac{12}{x}$

5. Determine which store offers the best buy. Show your work.

Store A	Store B	Store C
12 pencils for $2.40	10 pencils for $1.80	4 pencils for $1.00

6. Ben has taken 4 quizzes in math and earned grades of 80%, 85%, 92% and 75%. There is one more quiz in the term grading period. Ben wants to end the grading period with an average quiz grade of 85%.

   a. What is the lowest grade he can earn on Quiz 5 so that his quiz average is 85%?

   b. Think Beyond Is it possible for Ben to raise his quiz average for the term to 88%? Why or why not?

7. Lee bought yards of red and blue fabric to make several costumes for the school play. She bought 3 times as many yards of red fabric as blue fabric. She bought a total of 36 yards of fabric. How many yards of each color fabric did Lee buy?

   a. Use a bar diagram to represent this problem.

   b. Solve your problem.

8. The ratio of pepper plants to tomato plants in Nat's garden is 3 to 1.

Number of Pepper Plants	Number of Tomato Plants
	1
9	
	10
21	

a. Copy and complete the chart above showing different values for the numbers of pepper and tomato plants in Nat's garden.

b. Write an equation that expresses the relationship between the number of pepper plants (p) and the number of tomato plants (t) in Nat's garden.

SECTION 2

9. Ali, Bob, Chet and Didi recycle aluminum cans. They kept track of the number of cans they recycled last week and this week to see who made the most improvement in their recycling efforts.

Student	Last Week	This week
Ali	30	50
Bob	20	60
Chet	40	40
Didi	50	10

Who improved the most from last week to this week? Show or explain how you got your answer.

10. Examine this information about two brands of toothpaste.

Terrific Toothpaste	Tremendous Toothpaste
\$2.50 for 5 ounces	\$3 for 9 ounces

a. Find the unit rate of each brand of toothpaste in dollars per ounce.

b. Find the unit rate of each brand of toothpaste in ounces per dollar.

c. Which brand offers the better buy?

11. Earth revolves around the sun at the rate of 1,111 miles per minute.

a. Approximately how far does Earth revolve around the sun in 1 second? Show your work.

b. How far does Earth revolve around the sun in 1 hour? Show your work.

c. How long does it take Earth to revolve 1 mile around the sun? Show your work.

12. Copy and complete the table so that you can find the cost of 11 yards of fabric.

Yards of Fabric	3	6			
Cost	$22.50				

a. How did you decide which values to enter into the other columns in the table above?

b. Make a graph of price of fabric and cost.

c. Does it make sense to connect the points on your graph? Why or why not?

d. If you did connect the points, would they all fall on the same line? Why or why not?

e. Find a unit price for the fabric. Explain how you can use either the table or graph to find the unit price.

f. Write an explicit rule to find the cost (c) of any number of yards of fabric (n).

SECTION 3

13. Pictured below are three dot plots of three different data sets.

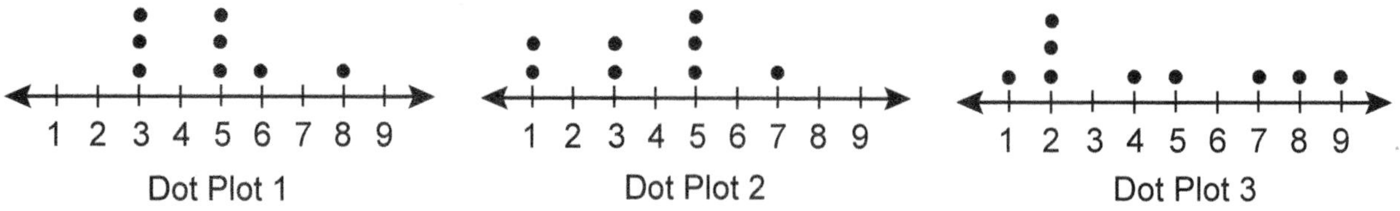

Determine whether each statement below accurately describes dot plot 1, dot plot 2, or dot plot 3.

a. The data set is bimodal..

b. The median value is not equal to one of the pieces of data in the set.

c. The median value is greater than the mode.

d. The range is 8.

14. The owners of the Fit and Fun Health Club lowered the heat in their indoor pool without telling their customers. They collected data to investigate whether the cooler temperature was affecting the time that their costumers spent in the pool. The day before they lowered the temperature, the owners kept track of the number of minutes each person spent in the pool from 12:00 to 1:00 pm. The day after they lowered the temperature, they did the same. The back-to-back stem-and-leaf plot shows the data that were collected.

Number of Minutes Spent in Pool

Before Lowering Temperature		After Lowering Temperature
9	0	5 5
5 5 5	1	0 0 5 5 8
8 6 6	2	0 5 7 7 9
9 5 0 0	3	5 5
5 5 5 3 0	4	5 5
9 7 6 1	5	0 0 5 6 7
0 0 0 0 0	6	0 0 0 7 8

a. Find the median of each data set.

b. Find the range of each data set.

c. Does it appear that the lower temperature has affected the time people spend in the pool? Why or why not?

d. Reread the paragraph about how the club owners collected the data for their statistical question. Why might the procedure they used lead to misleading conclusions about their costumers' use of the pool?

15. The histogram below shows the number of participating countries that sent different numbers of athletes to the London 2012 Summer Olympics.

London 2012 Summer Olympics

Frequency

160
150
140
130
120
110
100
90
80
70
60
50
40
30
20
10
0

0 50 100 150 200 250 300 350 400 450 500 550

Number of Athletes

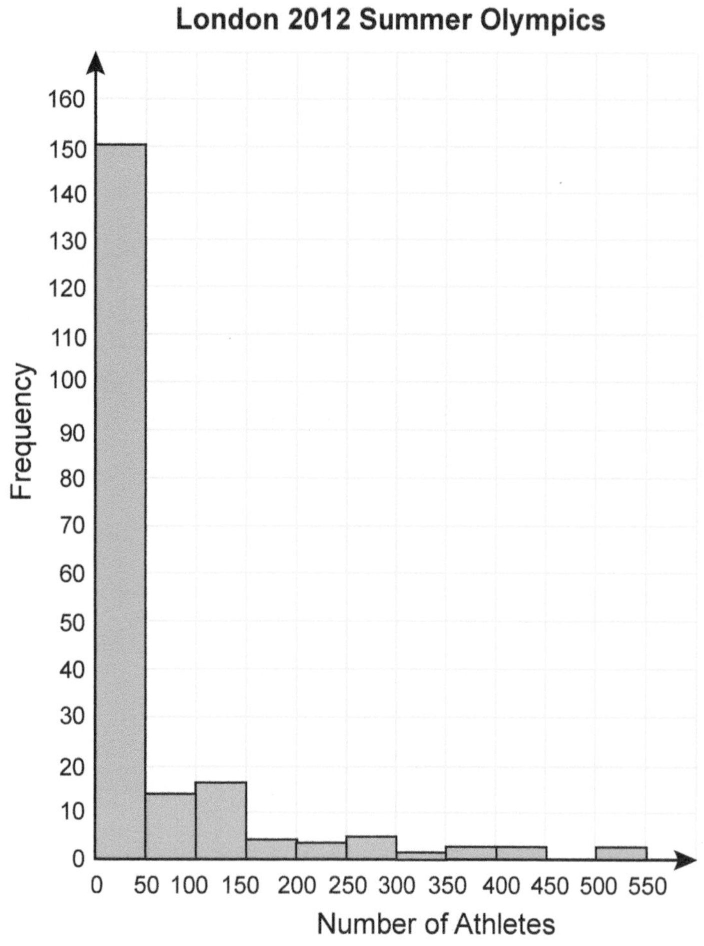

a. Write three statements that describe the distribution of the data.

b. Write a question about the data set that cannot be answered using this histogram.

c. The mean number of athletes sent to the Olympics by a participating country was 52. Do you think the mean is an accurate way to describe the data set? Why or why not?

16. During math class one day, Yalda and Doug were looking at the data sets below.

Data Set A: 21, 23, 25, 29, 29, 29, 32, 33, 34, 34, 35, 35, 823

Data Set B: 0, 0, 0, 16, 16, 17, 17, 18, 18, 19, 19, 20, 21, 22

Yalda looked at one of the data sets and said, "The mode is not a good representation of the typical value in this data set." Doug said, "The mean is not representative of the typical value in this data set." Which data set above do you think Yalda was looking at? Which data set do you think Doug was looking at? Explain your thinking.

17. One afternoon, students at Caldecott Middle School collected data about the time they spent waiting to use a computer in the library. Their data are shown below.

0, 0, 0, 0, 5, 7, 15, 15, 15, 16, 16, 17, 20

a. Find the five-number summary for this data set.

b. Use your five-number summary to create a box plot for the data set.

c. Find the interquartile range of the data set.

d. The students plan to use the data to argue that the school needs to buy another computer for the library. Which statistic(s) from Parts b and c could the students use to support their request for an additional computer? Explain your thinking.

e. Which statistic(s) from Parts b and c do not seem to support the students' request for an additional computer? Explain your thinking.

18. The librarian at the Pembroke Public Library made a box plot to show data about the ages of the people in the library one afternoon.

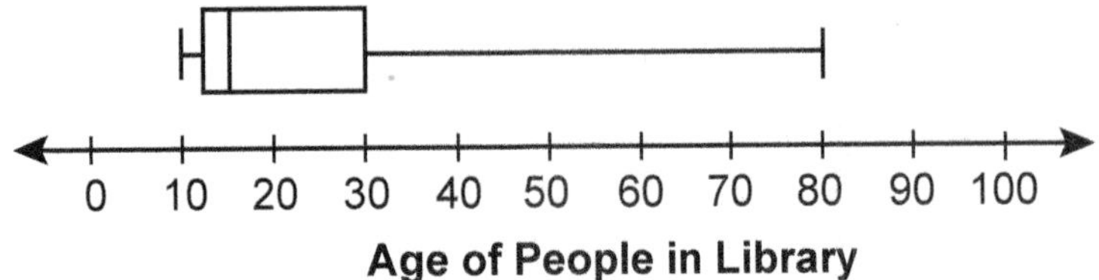

a. Use the box plot to fill in the blanks in the paragraph below.

The median age of the people in the data set was approximately __________ (i). The range of the ages was __________ (ii).

Fifty percent of the people were between __________ (iii) years and __________ (iv) years of age. Twenty-five percent of the people were at least __________ (v) years old.

b. Write one more sentence describing the data set and the ages of people in the library.

19. Ms. Lovell and Ms. Stefanik gave the same math quiz on Friday to their individual classes. The mean score in Ms. Lovell's class was 80 and the mean absolute deviation was 4.5. The mean score in Mrs. Stefanik's class was 81 and the mean absolute deviation was 9.0.

a. Interpret the mean score of each class.

b. Interpret the mean absolute deviation of each class.

c. Compare the data sets of the two classes. Is it accurate to say that one class did as well on the quiz as the other class? Why or why not?

Part 2. What went wrong?

20. Arturo's teacher asked him to find the measure of center of the data set below.

Time Students Spend Online per Day
30, 30, 40, 60, 65, 70, 75, 90, 120, 150

Arturo wrote, "According to the data set, students typically spend 30 minutes online each day because that value occurred more frequently than any of the others." Arturo's answer was marked wrong. Why? What is wrong with Arturo's reasoning?

21. Felicia's teacher asked her whether the mean or the median was the most appropriate measure of center for the data set below.

Number of Pets Students Own

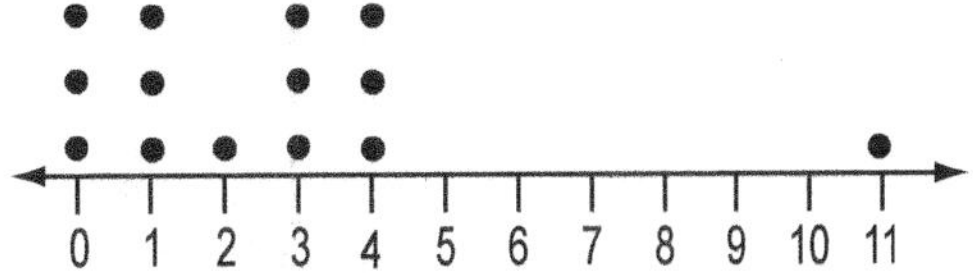

Number of Pets

Felicia said, "The median is not an accurate measure of center for this data set because the median is 2.5, and there is no such thing as 2.5 pets." What is wrong with Felicia's reasoning? What could you say to help her answer the question correctly?

22. Gaynor was asked to compare the gas mileage of two cars using the following information: Car A can travel 150 miles using 8 gallons of gas. Car B can travel 100 miles using 5 gallons of gas.

Car A $\frac{150}{8} = \frac{300}{16}$

Car B $\frac{100}{5} = \frac{300}{15}$

Gaynor concluded, "Car A has better gas mileage. 16 is greater than 15, so this must mean that Car A can go 1 more mile on the same amount of gas."

a. Write labels for each of the measures in the two proportions.

b. Use your answer from Part a to determine what is wrong with Gaynor's reasoning.

23. Louise was asked the following question on a recent quiz.

> Mary's homeroom has 12 girls and 16 boys. Which of the following classes has the same ratio of girls to boys?
>
> **A.** Mr. Sanchez
> 6 girls
> 10 boys
>
> **B.** Mr. Lee
> 9 girls
> 12 boys
>
> **C.** Ms. Gorlich
> 16 girls
> 12 boys
>
> **D.** Ms. Simmons
> 6 girls
> 4 boys

Louise chose answer A because she reasoned that Mary's homeroom has 4 more boys compared to girls, and the classroom in choice A also has 4 more boys than girls. What is wrong with Louise's reasoning?

24. Margot's teacher asked her to find the ratio of her height to her head circumference. Margot asked her teacher if she wanted her to use centimeters or inches. Margot's teacher said it wouldn't matter. Margot asked, "How could it not matter? Inches are bigger than centimeters, so I will get two different ratios." What is wrong with Margot's reasoning?

bimodal set A set that has two modes.

Example:
The set {1, 4, 6, 6, 6, 8, 8, 9, 9, 9, 10, 10} is bimodal with modes of 6 and 9.

bin An interval on a histogram

Example:
On the histogram shown there are 8 bins. The size of each bin is 10 minutes.

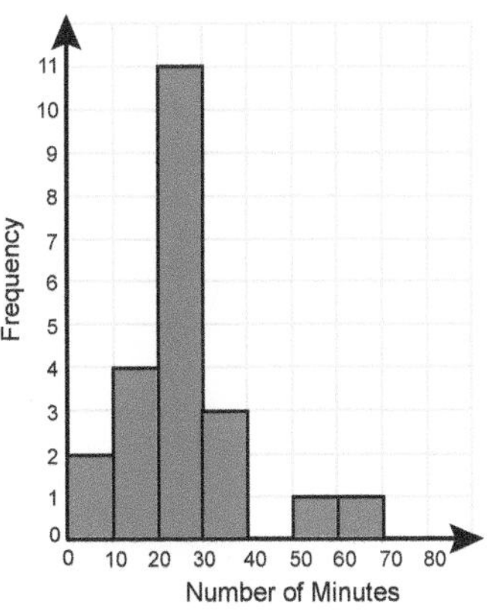

box-and-whisker plot (box plot) A diagram that summarizes a set of data using the median, the first and third quartiles, and the extreme values.

Example:
Box-and-whisker plot from data:
{53, 64, 76, 78, 79, 80, 83, 85, 86, 95, 98}

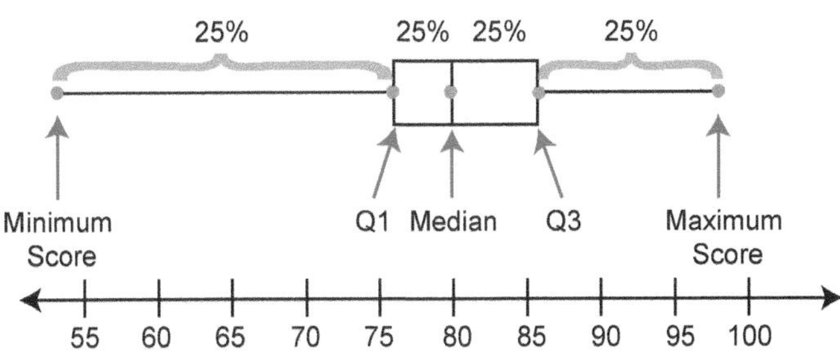

categorical data Data that can be categorized or grouped.

Example:
Birth month: January, February, March
Eye color: brown, blue, hazel, green
Grade Level: 7th grade, 8th grade, 9th grade

clusters A group of data points that lie within a small interval.

Example:
The set {1, 3, 4, 5, 6, 9, 10, 10, 20} has two clusters of data: {3, 4, 5, 6} and {9, 10, 10}.

concentration The measure or amount of one substance in a unit measure or given amount of another substance or solution.

Example:
The concentration of lemonade was 1 can frozen lemonade to 3 cans of water.

Even a small 0.3 mg/liter concentration of iron in a well can cause the water to look rusty.

data Facts or numbers that describe something such as people, places and things.

Example:
Pay per hour: \$5.75, \$10.00, \$23.00, \$55.15
Education level: 8th grade, high school, college
Population: 15 thousand, 3.75 million, 1 billion

deviation from the mean The distance of a data point from the mean value of a data set.

Example:
The set {1, 4, 5, 6, 8, 9, 9, 10, 11} has a mean of 7 and the deviation of the point 4 from the mean is 3.

distribution of data The spread of a data set as described by measures or descriptors.

Example:
The distribution of the set {1, 3, 4, 5, 6, 9, 10, 10, 20} is described by the following:

- range is 20 − 1 = 19
- clusters exist at {3, 4, 5, 6} and {9, 10, 10}
- gaps occur between 1 and 3, between 6 and 9 and between 10 and 20
- the point 20 appears to be an outlier

dot plot A graph showing the frequency of values in a data set along a number line using a dot (•) to indicate data points. Sometimes referred to as a line plot when an X is used to indicate data points. Dot plots are used to graph small sets of data.

Example:
Set C: {1, 2, 6, 4, 2, 3, 2, 4}
The pot dot for Set C is:

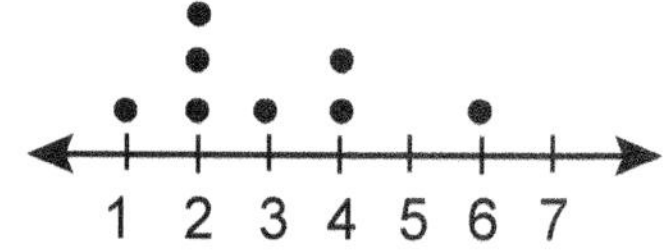

equivalent ratios Different ratio representations of the same multiplicative comparison.

Example:

$\frac{5}{8} = \frac{15}{24} = \frac{55}{88} = \frac{0.625}{1}$

11:2 = 33:6 = 121:22 = 5.5:1

first or lower quartile, Q1 The median of the data values below the median of the entire data set.

Example:
The set {1, 4, 5, 6, 8, 9, 9, 10, 11} has a median of 8 and the Q1 value is 4.5, the median of the set {1, 4, 5, 6}.

five-number summary A summary description of a data set that includes the minimum value, Q1 value, median value, Q3 value and maximum value.

Example:
The five-number summary of the set {1, 4, 5, 6, 8, 9, 9, 10, 11} is:
Minimum = 1, Q1 = 4.5, Median = 8, Q3 = 9.5, Maximum = 11

frequency The number of times an event occurs.

Example:
The results of tossing a coin 5 times were: HHTTT. The frequency of H was 2 and the frequency of T was 3.

gap An interval that includes no data points.

Example:
The set {1, 3, 4, 5, 6, 9, 10, 10, 20} has gaps between 1 and 3, between 6 and 9 and between 10 and 20.

histogram A graphical presentation of numerical data displayed in intervals on one axis and the frequency of observations within those intervals on the other axis.

Example:

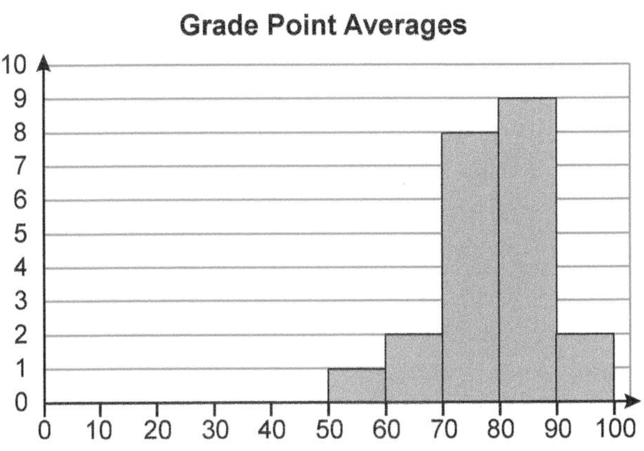

interquartile range The distance between the Q1 value and Q3 value of a data set.

Example:
The set {1, 4, 5, 6, 8, 9, 9, 10, 11} has a median of 8, a Q1 value of 4.5 and a Q3 value of 9.5. The interquartile range is $9.5 - 4.5 = 5$.

mean The arithmetic average of a set of numbers.

Example:
The mean of {4, 8, 2, 10, 15} is
$\frac{4 + 8 + 2 + 10 + 15}{5} = 7.8$.

mean absolute deviation A method for measuring the spread (variability) in a set of data by calculating the average distance each data point is from the mean.

Example:
The set {1, 4, 5, 6, 8, 9, 9, 10, 11} has a mean of 7. The difference of 1 and the mean is $^-6$ $(1 - 7 = {}^-6)$ and the difference of 10 and the mean is 3 $(10 - 7 = 3)$. The absolute value of each of the differences is used to calculate the sum of the deviations. The sum of the deviations is 24 and the mean absolute deviation is $24 \div 9$ or 2.67.

measures of center Numerical values used to summarize or describe the overall "average" of a data set.

Example:
The most common measures of center are the mean and median.

median The middle data value when the data points are arranged in order. If a data set has an even number of values, the median is the mean of the two middle values.

Example:
The median of {2, 4, 8, 10, 15} is 8.
The median of {5, 5, 8, 14, 20, 21} is $\frac{8 + 14}{2} = 11$.

mode The most frequent value in a data set.

Example:
The mode of {5, 5, 8, 14, 20, 21} is 5.

The set {3, 3, 3, 5, 6, 7, 7, 7, 9} is bimodal and has modes of 3 and 7.

The set {2, 4, 8, 10, 15} has no mode.

---

numerical data Data representing a quantity or quality that can be measured or counted.

Example:
Height: 38", 48", 56", 65"
Age: 11, 13, 21, 35, 54
Number of family members: 2, 4, 5, 7

---

part-to-part ratio A ratio comparing a part or portion of a group or collection to another part or portion of the group or collection. A part-to-part ratio is often written using the colon notation $a : b$, read "*a* to *b*."

Example:
Of 15 balloons in a bunch, 5 were yellow, 6 were red and 4 were blue. The ratio of red balloons to yellow balloons was 6 : 5 ("six to five").

At lunch, 3 friends ate sandwiches and 2 ate pasta. The ratio of sandwich eaters to pasta eaters was 3 : 2 ("three to two").

---

part-to-whole ratio A ratio comparing a part or portion of a group or collection to the entire group or collection. A part-to-whole ratio is often written using the fraction notation $\frac{a}{b}$, read "*a* to *b*."

Example:
Of 15 balloons in a bunch, 5 were yellow, 6 were red and 4 were blue. The ratio of red balloons to total balloons was $\frac{6}{15}$ ("six to fifteen" or 6 : 15).

At lunch, 3 friends ate sandwiches and 2 ate pasta. The ratio of sandwich eaters to friends was $\frac{3}{5}$ ("three to five" or 3 : 5).

---

population density The ratio of the number of people living in an area to the size of that area expressed as persons per unit area.

Example:
The population density of New York City is greater than 3,200 persons per square mile or 3,200 people : 1 sq. mi.

Mongolia has the smallest population density of any country with only 4.3 persons per square mile or 4.3 people : 1 sq. mi.

---

profit The difference, when it is positive, between income and cost.

Example:
The team bought T-shirts for \$6 each and sold them for \$10 each, making a profit of \$4 on each T-shirt sold.

Luke spent \$15 on gas and was paid \$45 for mowing lawns. He made a profit of \$30.

proportion An equation stating that two ratios are equal.

Example:
$\frac{a}{b} = \frac{c}{d}$ or $a:b = c:d$
$\frac{2}{7} = \frac{8}{28}$

range The difference between the maximum value and the minimum value in the data set.

Example:
The set $\{1, 3, 4, 5, 6, 9, 10, 10, 20\}$ has a range of $20 - 1 = 19$.

rate A comparison or relationship between two quantities usually having different units of measure.

Example:
The average rate of a car that traveled 60 miles in 2 hours was $\frac{60 \text{ mi.}}{2 \text{ hr.}} = 30$ mph ("thirty miles per hour").

Jenna's pay rate for babysitting was $\frac{\$7}{1 \text{ hr.}}$ ("seven dollars per hour").

ratio A comparison or relationship of two quantities, a and b, stated as "a to b" and represented as $a:b$ or $\frac{a}{b}$.

Example:
The ratio representing the number of cars in a parking lot to the total number of their wheels is $\frac{1}{4}$, or "one to four."

In a recipe calling for 3 cups of flour and 2 cups of sugar, the ratio of flour to sugar is 3:2, or "three to two."

scaling down Dividing all numbers in a ratio by the same number greater than 1 to get an equivalent ratio consisting of smaller numbers.

Example:
Scale $\frac{4}{16}$ down by 2 to obtain $\frac{2}{8}$ or by 4 to obtain $\frac{1}{4}$.

A punch recipe that serves 20 people calls for 6 cups of ginger ale for every 4 cups of juice. In order to make punch for 10 people, scale down the ratio of ginger ale to juice; $\frac{6}{4} \div \frac{2}{2} = \frac{3 \text{ cups ginger ale}}{2 \text{ cups juice}}$.

scaling up Multiplying all numbers in a ratio by the same number greater than 1 to get an equivalent ratio consisting of larger numbers.

Example:
Scale $\frac{2}{5}$ up by 3 to obtain $\frac{6}{15}$ or by 10 to obtain $\frac{20}{50}$.

A cake recipe calls for 1 cup of sugar for every 2 cups of flour. In order to make 3 cakes, scale up the ratio of sugar to flour; $\frac{1}{2} \cdot \frac{3}{3} = \frac{3 \text{ cups sugar}}{6 \text{ cups flour}}$.

scatter plot The graph of a set of ordered pairs on a coordinate plane.

Example:

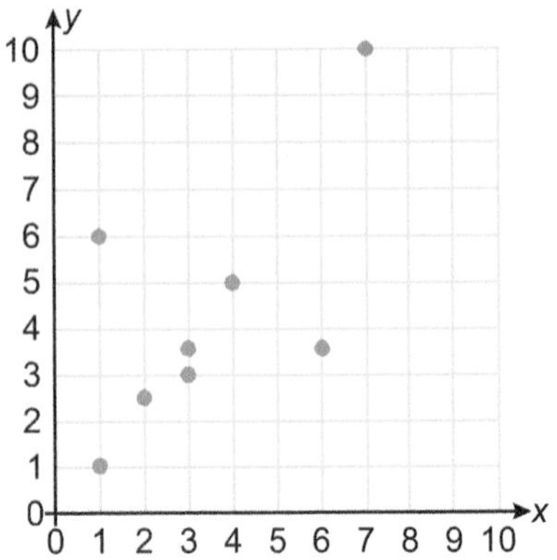

simplest form (of a fraction) A fraction whose numerator and denominator have no common factors (except 1).

Example:

$\frac{2}{3}$ is the simplest form of $\frac{8}{12} = \frac{10}{15} = \frac{16}{24}$.

$\frac{7}{11}$ is the simplest form of $\frac{14}{22} = \frac{35}{55} = \frac{63}{99}$.

Sandy counted 10 cars in the parking lot and 40 wheels to write a ratio of 10 cars : 40 wheels or $\frac{10}{40}$. In simplest form this ratio is $\frac{1}{4}$.

stem-and-leaf plot A display of a data set organized in rows to show distribution by separating the last digits (leaves) from the previous digits (stem).

Example:

Data set {72, 76, 78, 79, 81, 86, 88, 88, 95, 98}:

Stem	Leaves
7	2 6 8 9
8	1 6 8 8
9	5 8

Key: 7 | 2 represents 72.

Data set {123, 125, 128, 134, 157, 159}:

Stem	Leaves
12	3 5 8
13	4
15	7 9

Key: 12 | 3 represents 123.

third or upper quartile, Q3 The median of the data values above the median of the entire set.

Example:

The set {1, 4, 5, 6, 8, 9, 9, 10, 11} has a median of 8 and the Q3 value is 9.5, the median of the set {9, 9, 10, 11}.

unit price The cost for one item or one unit.	**Example**: The unit price for grapes was $2.99 per pound. An office store advertised 5 notebooks for $6.25. The unit price for notebooks was $1.25 each.
unit rate A rate for a single unit of time or measure.	**Example**: A car drove 120 miles in 2 hours for a unit rate of 60 miles per hour (or 60 mph). Over the 120 miles, the car used 5 gallons of gas for a unit rate of 24 miles per gallon (or 24 mpg).

Hints

Lesson 1.2

Parts and Wholes

Page 10, Start It Off: How many vases will be needed?

On Your Own

Page 17, Question 2e: Use a chart to scale up the ratio and compare the number of boys and girls using subtraction.

Page 17, Question 4d: Use a chart to scale up the ratio and use subtraction to compare the number of boys and girls.

Page 19, Question 15: Draw a diagram. How many peanuts should you use?

Lesson 1.3

Human Proportions

Page 23, Question 2: Scale up da Vinci's ratio. Write both scaled-up ratios as fractions. Then compare the fractions.

Page 23, Question 5: The ear is $\frac{1}{3}$ the length of the face and the face is $\frac{1}{10}$ of his height.

Page 24, Wrap It Up: How many inches are there in 6 feet?

Lesson 1.5

Fair Shares for a Fundraiser

Page 35, Question 1: What part of the total lawn did Chloe mow?

Page 36, Question 3a: How many total hours did the students work?

Oobleck Ratios

Page 37, Question 5d: How many cups of cornstarch are in 10 pounds?

Page 38, Question 5e: Write each recipe as a ratio of cornstarch to water in fraction form. Scale up or down to get whole numbers for both the cornstarch and water. Compare the fractions.

On Your Own

Page 40, Question 4c: 1 cup = 16 tablespoons

Page 40, Question 5b: 5,280 feet = 1 mile
The Empire State Building is less than $\frac{1}{4}$ mile tall.

Page 41, Question 10: Change all values to the same unit first.

Lesson 2.1

Comparing Rates

Page 61, Question 3c: 2,000 pounds = 1 ton

Lesson 2.3

Popular Punch

Page 78, Question 4f: 1 cup = 16 tablespoons

On Your Own

Page 80, Question 3a: 1 ton = 2,000 pounds

Lesson 3.3

On Your Own

Page 111, Question 1: Would you describe it as the middle value in the set?

Index

A

B

C

D

E

F